The Open University

U116

Environment: journeys through a changing world

Block 2
Arctic approach

Parts 1–4

Joe Smith, Mark Brandon and Matthew Kurtz

This publication forms part of the Open University course U116 *Environment: journeys through a changing world*. Details of this and other Open University courses can be obtained from the Student Registration and Enquiry Service, The Open University, PO Box 197, Milton Keynes MK7 6BJ, United Kingdom (tel. +44 (0)845 300 60 90; email general-enquiries@open.ac.uk).

Alternatively, you may visit the Open University website at www.open.ac.uk where you can learn more about the wide range of courses and packs offered at all levels by The Open University.

To purchase a selection of Open University course materials visit www.ouw.co.uk, or contact Open University Worldwide, Walton Hall, Milton Keynes MK7 6AA, United Kingdom for a brochure (tel. +44 (0)1908 858793; fax +44 (0)1908 858787; email ouw-customer-services@open.ac.uk).

The Open University
Walton Hall, Milton Keynes
MK7 6AA

First published 2009.

Edited and designed by The Open University.

Typeset by SR Nova Pvt. Ltd, Bangalore, India.

Printed and bound in the United Kingdom by Halstan Printing Group, Amersham.

ISBN 978 0 7492 2087 7

1.1

Contents

Introduction to Block 2

The title of this block, *Arctic approach*, suggests an exploration in a new territory. It is the first stop on your intellectual journey as you investigate environmental issues with U116. The title also hints at the way in which the block explores different approaches to understanding environments and environmental change. The opening block of the course helped you prepare to set out from home: it helped you to orientate yourself. It gave a sense of how you as a student of environmental issues need to engage with science, technology and social science approaches in order to make sense of environmental questions. It helped you get your bearings in both time and space.

However, Block 1 leaves some large questions about how we come to know about environments and environmental problems. This block will take you on a journey through the varied ways in which environmental issues are understood: by explorers, mapmakers, artists and journalists in Part 1, *Imagining the Arctic*; by natural scientists in Parts 2, *Time in context* and 3, *Following the flows*; and by social scientists and indigenous Arctic peoples in Part 4, *Ways of knowing the Arctic*. The block does not promote the idea that one of these perspectives is more 'right' than another, although the balance of the block gives more space (in Parts 2 and 3) to the work of natural scientists. This is because their work has been central to revealing the global environmental problems that are so prominent in the course.

Before you embark on your own journey to the Arctic, you may like to follow the experiences of an expedition of scientists and artists to West Greenland. The course DVD contains a map showing the expedition route and you can watch interviews given along the journey. Some of the interviews illustrate differences between indigenous and 'southern' and also between scientific and artistic ways of thinking about the Arctic and environmental change.

Introduction to Block 2

Part 1
Imagining the Arctic

Joe Smith

Introduction

1

The authors of this block have chosen to take you on a journey to the Arctic. The composite satellite image shown in Figure 1.1 shows the Earth from space at night. The image, which was made by 'stitching together' images of sections of the Earth, shows both land masses and the sparkle of the world's cities. It is taken from what is for many people an unfamiliar angle, with the satellite taking images from the 'top of the world', making the Arctic the centre of our view of the Earth. The Arctic's status as one of the last wilderness areas on the planet is easy to appreciate from this picture.

The region has become an important location for current environmental science. The effects of climate change particularly are more evident here than anywhere else on the planet. Yet it has also long held a powerful place in the western imagination in terms of the exploration and exploitation of the natural world. It is also a place that is best understood by bringing together very different accounts of the same place (artistic and descriptive; journalistic and scientific; *indigenous* and 'western'). For all these reasons the Arctic makes for an important and revealing first stopping point on your itinerary.

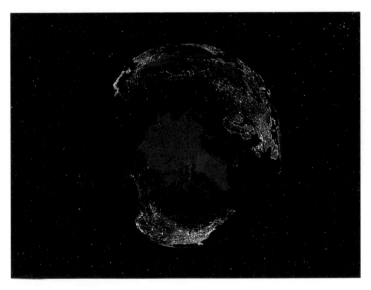

Figure 1.1 NASA's 'Earthlights' image of the Earth from the North Pole that 'maps' economic development by showing artificial lights at night

---

Activity 1.1   Imagining the Arctic

Without doing any research, jot down responses to the following questions:

1 What three images come to mind when you hear the word 'Arctic'?

2 What five names, other words, or phrases do you first think of when you read the word 'Arctic'?

3 What was the last news story you can recall about the Arctic?

4 Which nation states have territory within the region defined as 'the Arctic'?

Discussion

One of the course team asked a family member and this is what they came up with:

1 iceberg; polar bear; igloo

2 polar bear; igloo; *Titanic*; midnight sun; Amundsen

3 a story about the continued shrinking of Arctic summer sea ice

4 countries: Russia, Canada, Norway… USA. What about Inuit?

There is a good chance that you have included polar bears and igloos. The news stories will be diverse, but for the last few years many of these stories relate in one way or another to climate change or fossil fuel resources. These are issues that have thrust the polar regions into the spotlight. The countries you thought of may have included: Canada, Denmark/Greenland/Faroe Islands, Finland, Iceland, Norway, Sweden, The Russian Federation and the USA. These are members of the Arctic Council, an international body which allows governments and other interested parties in the Arctic regions to debate and collaborate. The countries are joined on the Arctic Council by representative bodies of indigenous Arctic peoples.

Your knowledge of, and feelings about, the Arctic will come from many sources, including television, radio, the internet and newspapers. But the Arctic has a much deeper hold on our culture: it also appears in books, artworks and songs. It is interesting to think that children all over the world are often as familiar with the idea of an igloo or a polar bear as they are with some of the buildings or animals they live near. Section 3 will look further into how our ideas of the Arctic are shaped by the media and by creative works of the imagination.

Before that though, Section 2 will help you to orientate yourself and also get you thinking about how different people with different intentions or needs represent environments through maps in varied ways.

Mapping the Arctic

2

2.1 What is a map?

When preparing for a journey to a new place most people start by reaching for a map. But what is a map? The sort that most of us are most familiar with is a diagram that attempts to represent aspects of the Earth's surface. This section will look at a number of maps of the Arctic as a way of introducing the place, its people, and some of the prominent issues explored in this block.

It is easy to forget that maps can never be completely accurate recreations of the world: they are just marks on a page or pixels on a screen. Whether they are hand-drawn or the product of a satellite's orbit they are versions of the way the world is, rather than exact reproductions. They are the work of human creativity and imagination as well as careful measurement. Maps are models of the world: much like model aeroplanes, they are smaller representations that can vary greatly in their level of detail and accuracy. The aspects that their creators choose to emphasise, or at which to point the lens, and the dimensions they ignore, illuminate their priorities. The diverse and sometimes contrasting ways of knowing and representing the world are revealed in similarly varied maps.

One of the most important map-makers in European history is Gerard Mercator. He created the map of the Arctic lands that appears in Figure 1.2

Figure 1.2 Mercator's map of the Arctic lands, 'Polus Artieus', from the 1595 edition of his world map

as part of the publication of his first world map of 1569. Mercator based it on existing maps, accounts by English explorers of the North Atlantic, including a fourteenth-century monk, and his own theories on the location of the magnetic North Pole. He envisaged four seemingly habitable islands surrounding a black magnetic mountain (the pole). It is clearly a product of imagination and reported knowledge rather than direct observation. Such maps were not driven simply by curiosity: they were part of the European drive to colonise resource-rich territories.

There is an important and revealing detail in Mercator's map: the lines that start at the North Pole (the lines of longitude) and the successively larger circles that surround it (the lines of latitude). These map-making devices are crucial to anyone wanting to understand their position on the globe, whether they are walkers in the Peak District of the UK or environmental scientists working at the North or South Pole.

Box 1.1   Carving up the planet

The terms latitude and longitude specify locations on the Earth. On most maps you can see both vertical and horizontal lines dividing up the regions. The lines that run from east to west in the plots are called lines of *latitude*, and the lines that run north to south are called lines of *longitude*. You can see this in Figure 1.3, where the vertical red lines are the lines of longitude, and the horizontal blue lines are the lines of latitude.

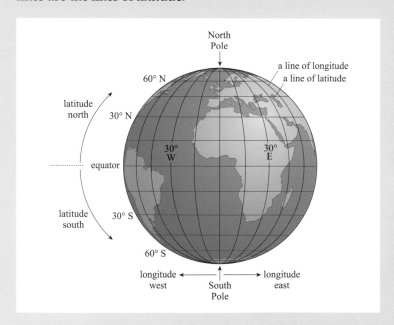

Figure 1.3 The lines of longitude and latitude on planet Earth as viewed from above the equator

If you take a round fruit such as an apple and draw equally spaced lines equivalent to the blue latitude lines in Figure 1.3, and then slice the apple along these lines, you can see that each slice will have the same width of skin because the blue latitude lines are equal distances apart. On the Earth the distance between the middle (the equator at 0° latitude) and the very 'top' (the North Pole at 90° latitude) is divided up into 90 lines called degrees of latitude approximately 110 km apart.

If you take another apple and draw some lines like the red longitude lines in Figure 1.4, and cut the fruit along them, this time you would end up with wedges. If you think about the wedges and the skin width, where the middle of the fruit was (the equator on Earth) the width of skin is greatest, while at both ends the width of the skin reduces to zero. You can see this clearly in this view of the Earth from the North Pole.

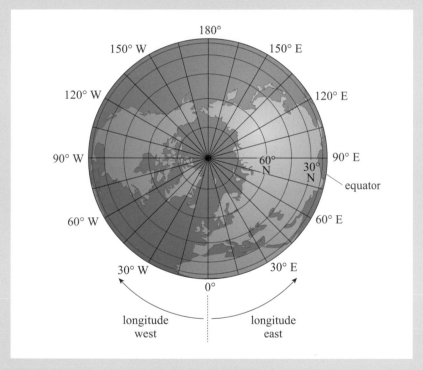

Figure 1.4 The lines of longitude and latitude on planet Earth as viewed from above the North Pole

In the view in Figure 1.3 you can see that the blue lines of latitude are always the same distance apart, whereas the distance between the red lines of longitude reduces towards each pole, where they meet. The Earth is divided into 360 of these lines, called degrees of longitude. At the equator the distance between each line is 110 km, but the further you get from the equator the shorter the distance between the lines of longitude becomes. In London the distance between each line of longitude is about 70 km. It would take a very long time to walk around the world at the equator, but at the North Pole you could do it in just seconds. For historical reasons the 0° longitude line runs through Greenwich in London and, looking down from the North Pole in a clockwise direction, the degrees of longitude range from 0 to +180° (by convention we call this the western hemisphere), and in an anticlockwise direction they range from 0 to −180° (the eastern hemisphere).

If I gave you my location in degrees latitude and longitude you could see exactly where I was on Earth – for example, I am writing this from approximately 52° N 0° E, which is in Cambridge, England. It is important to remember that the distance between each degree of latitude is always the same wherever it is on the planet, whilst one degree of longitude varies depending on the latitude at which it is measured.

The very varied maps of the Arctic regions that you will consider in this section offer a means of exploring different ways of knowing about environments and environmental change. People often think of maps as more or less accurate representations of the world around them, and as a tool to carry out a task; for example, most people are familiar with maps as a way of finding their way on a journey. Maps have often had their origins in the need to arrange the legally binding division of land, whether at the level of the nation state or the rural parish.

However, maps can never fully represent the world; they are no more than the best effort of the human intellect as someone tries to summarise something for a particular purpose. The more ambitious maps, whether in terms of accuracy or scale, have always been expensive to produce, and hence have needed patrons. Today these patrons range from millions of motorists paying for satellite navigation devices, to local authorities and national governments. On other occasions it is international agencies or global corporations who pay for mapping. As you consider the different representations of the Arctic in this section, take note of the varied intentions of the map-makers (often called cartographers) and their patrons.

Activity 1.2   Everyday maps

Which maps are important in your everyday experience? Note that this does not necessarily mean maps that you use every day. I mean, rather, our commonplace experience of maps. Take ten minutes to make a quick list of maps that you experience in this way.

Discussion

Were you surprised, when you actually started to identify the common use of maps, at just how much they are part of our everyday experience? The kinds of thing you might have noted could include: Ordnance Survey maps; newspaper, TV or online weather maps; 'You are Here' maps in towns or shopping centres; road maps; travel brochures; GPS (Global Positioning System) in cars. You may well have thought of others. For some of these, such as GPS-generated maps, latitude and longitude are vital. For others, such as a sketch map made by a friend that details how to find a shop, scale and precise measurement are almost irrelevant: all you need are some landmarks shown along the way.

Box 1.2   Flat maps of a spherical world?

Fundamental to producing a map is the relationship between data (the information you wish to display and convey) and space, both the geographic space being represented and the space available on a sheet of paper or display screen. Data is represented by points (to show location) and lines (to show connections or borders), by symbols (to convey features), and by names and colour and/or shading (to represent areas). Of course, the names of places, like Milton Keynes, don't appear on the ground where they are shown on maps! These are the codes that are part of the language of maps.

One of the challenges facing cartographers as they try to express both data and space at the largest scales (i.e. the whole Earth or large sections of it) is the classic problem of representing features on the curved surface of a spheroidal Earth (or globe, see Figure 1.8) on a plane (or flat) surface. The point is that, no matter how we represent the world on a flat surface, we lose some major property of scale or shape. Mercator's projection (Figure 1.5) successfully represented direction, was quite good for shape with smaller outlines, but was bad for area and distance. So, for example, it makes Greenland and Antarctica look very much bigger than they really are, and land masses near the equator smaller. Of the many attempts to improve on the Mercator projection, one of the most commonly used is the Peters projection (Figure 1.6), which elongates land masses but is better than Mercator in terms of expressing area.

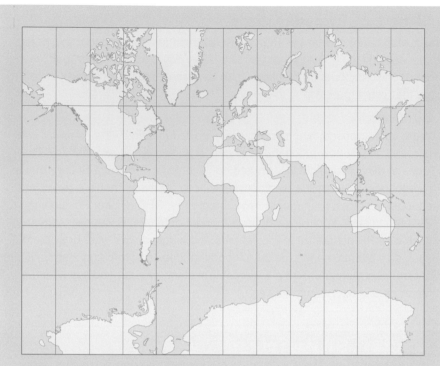

Figure 1.5 The Mercator projection

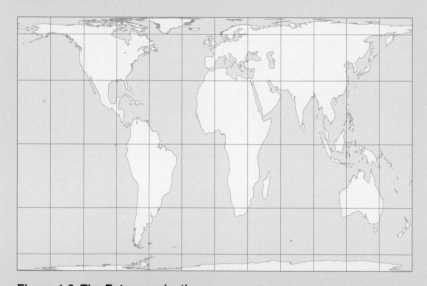

Figure 1.6 The Peters projection

You can demonstrate this at your kitchen table by slitting the skin of an orange in segments from top (at the stalk) to bottom and then trying to press the resulting pieces of orange peel on to a flat surface. The skin bulges up a bit, and there are gaps. Some cartographers have produced world maps that do resemble peeled oranges. These are called interrupted sinusoidal or Sanson–Flamsteed projections (Figure 1.7). The more segments of the 'orange' you cut, the better the representation of surface area.

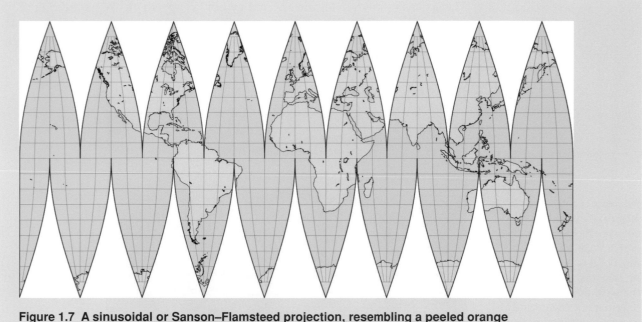

Figure 1.7 A sinusoidal or Sanson–Flamsteed projection, resembling a peeled orange

Figure 1.8 Maps of the world are very familiar to us – they appear everywhere. But we often forget how much ingenuity has gone into expressing the physical and other features of the world in abstract ways

2.2 Defining the Arctic

How would you know you were in the Arctic? Imagine walking along a stony beach. It is a clear, sunny day, the sky is blue and there is a chill in the air – just like the cold you get on a summer morning before the Sun has warmed up the day. Familiar so far, but look around to take in a little more of what you can see on this particular beach. The water is relatively calm and there are ice floes grounded at the water's edge, with small icebergs just offshore. Icebergs on a beach? Walk on further. There are tree trunks scattered along the beach, but looking landwards you cannot see any trees. Behind the beach there are bare, smooth hills with wide, softly shaped valleys. The north-facing gullies on the hills are filled with snow.

The scene is shown in Figure 1.9, and by now I expect you are wondering where you are. If I carried on describing the scene, by the time I got to the polar bear footprints in the few patches of sand and the walrus basking on the beach you might guess that I am describing an Arctic scene. But what makes this an Arctic place? Is it the icebergs, or the snow, and why are there trees here? (The Arctic driftwood is a puzzle that will be answered in Part 2.)

Svalbard is a group of islands about halfway between Norway and the North Pole. Although most of it is uninhabited by humans, it is home to the northernmost bank, newspaper, cinema and indoor swimming pool, and its road signs include a unique warning concerning polar bears.

Figure 1.9 A photograph of a typical scene on a Svalbard beach (Norway)

The Arctic region is defined in various ways. For climatologists it is understood as the area between the North Pole and the northern *treeline*. Figure 1.10 shows the exception that proves the rule: a lone tree near a town in Alaska, which has been humorously dubbed the Kotzebue National Forest. Although a photograph can help to capture a sense of a place it is limited in a number of ways. It is through maps that people have sought to communicate a richer and fuller body of information about what a place is like and where it is in relation to other places.

Figure 1.10 The exception that proves the rule: a lone tree that survives north of the treeline in Kotzebue, Alaska

Activity 1.3   Marking out the Arctic on a map

Look at Figure 1.11 and take a moment to note where the 10 °C *isotherm* and the treeline are close and where they are far apart, and how they relate to the latitude of the Arctic Circle. An isotherm is a line joining places of equal temperature.

Discussion

The lines actually match pretty well considering that the growth of trees is not linked to temperature alone. In North America, Canada and Siberia, especially along the coasts, the lines seem particularly close together. The only significant divergence is in Russia between the longitudes of about 30° and 90° E, where the treeline is much further south than the 10 °C isotherm. The map shows that Iceland is south of the treeline, and the reason why there are not many trees there today is because humans deforested the land in previous centuries. Making a sweeping generalisation, both the treeline and the 10 °C isotherm are generally north of the Arctic Circle (66.6° N), with the exception of eastern Canada, Greenland, Iceland and the area of divergence of the two lines in Russia.

Earlier in this section, one definition of the Arctic region was the area north of the treeline. The Arctic is also popularly understood as the area north of the Arctic Circle; that is, the line drawn at 66.6° north of the equator. The Arctic Circle marks the southern limit of the 'polar day' and 'polar night', the twenty-four hours of daylight (summer) and night (winter) that those latitudes experience. However, another widely used definition amongst polar scientists is the area where the average temperature for the warmest month (July) is below 10 °C. Hence the brown dashed and pink lines in Figure 1.11 offer two possible definitions of the Arctic.

Although the treeline and 10 °C isotherm do not map exactly on to one another, they both offer fairly clear definitions (albeit, in the case of the treeline, one that has to 'guess' the equivalent of the treeline over the oceanic portions). But both of these definitions mean that the maps have to acknowledge that the boundaries of the region will move with climate change. This is not a boundary that humans have marked, but one that is dictated by environmental processes. In other words, this is a line drawn by nature – by the living world.

Another way of mapping the Arctic region is to consider who lives there and where, as shown in Figure 1.12.

The Earthlights image shown at the start of this block shows that the Arctic region's thirty million square km is extremely sparsely populated compared with the cities in the populous temperate regions to the south. However, Figure 1.12 shows that the Arctic is far from empty or uninhabited in human terms. It also demonstrates that the indigenous peoples of the Arctic are culturally diverse. The region has a population of four million, including more than thirty different indigenous peoples and many languages. A similar map of the plant and animal life of the region would also confirm that it is far from being a sparsely populated place. Indeed, the Inuit and other indigenous communities have found plenty to live off for millennia, and view the region as far from empty.

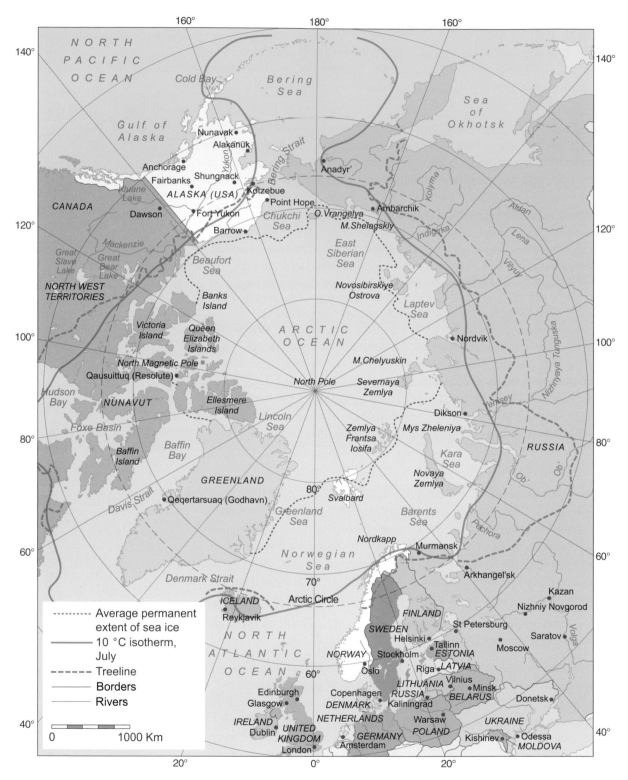

Figure 1.11 A map showing nation states, the Arctic Circle (thin dashed line), the treeline (brown dashed line) and the 10 °C isotherm (in pink): another way of defining the Arctic. Specific locations mentioned in the block are emphasised on the map, including Svalbard and Kotzebue. *(Source: adapted from http://nsidc.org/arcticmet/ arctic_map.html, accessed November 2008)*

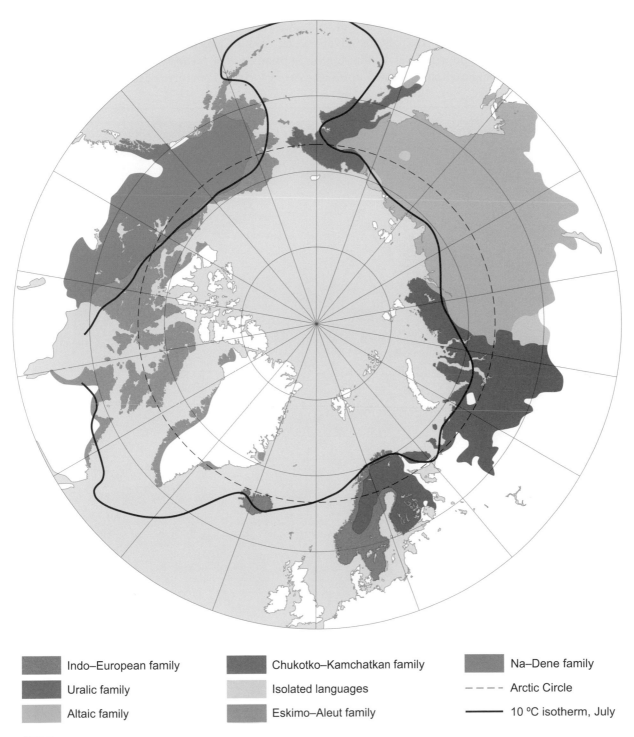

	Indo–European family		Chukotko–Kamchatkan family		Na–Dene family
	Uralic family		Isolated languages	- - -	Arctic Circle
	Altaic family		Eskimo–Aleut family	———	10 ºC isotherm, July

Notes:
Areas show colours according to the original languages of the respective indigenous people, even if they do not speak their languages today. Overlapping populations are not shown. The map does not claim to show exact boundaries between the individual language groups. Typical colonial populations, which are not traditional Arctic populations, are not shown (Danes in Greenland, Russians in the Russian Federation, non-native Canadians and Americans in North America).

Figure 1.12 Arctic peoples map showing language families. Although there are overlaps, the coloured areas are a useful quick indicator of the fact that the indigenous peoples of the Arctic are culturally diverse and do not map tidily on to the much more recently drawn political boundaries. *(Source: adapted from http://arctic-council.org/filearchive/AHDRmap_lan-3..jpg, accessed November 2008)*

Charting the contours of the region, both above and below the waterline, shows that the Arctic is also diverse in terms of its physical form, and is not just the expanse of flat ice that we might imagine. The *bathymetric map* in Figure 1.13 shows the contours under the Arctic Ocean. This form of mapping has

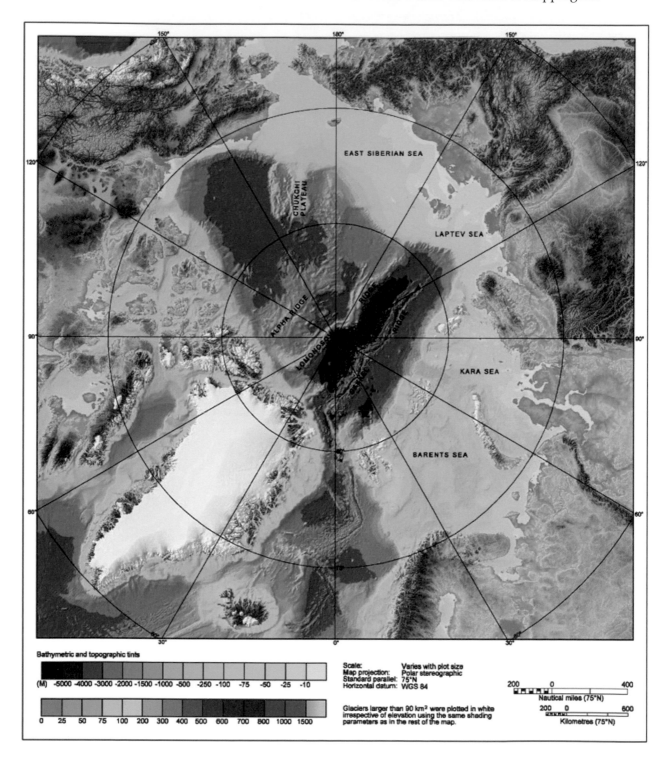

taken on a more urgent political significance in the early years of the twenty-first century as some national governments (for example Russia, Canada and the US) prepare for disputes about sovereignty and access to mineral wealth in the region.

The kinds of animated map shown in Figures 1.14 and 1.15 are useful for three reasons. In terms of this block they clearly demonstrate that the Arctic environment is dynamic – that is, it is constantly changing. But they also make a more general point about the fact that new forms of mapping based on satellite images and geographic information systems (GIS) can communicate some things that static maps cannot. Finally, these maps give you access to up-to-date information on the changes in annual sea ice extent. Less ice may accelerate climate change, but also opens up access to new shipping lanes such as the Northwest Passage, and access to untapped mineral resources.

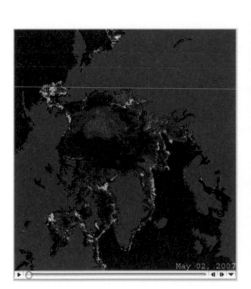
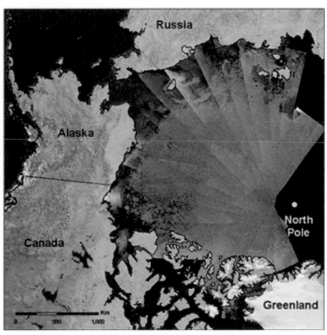

Figures 1.14 and 1.15 These stills are taken from animations presented on the website of the US National Snow and Ice Data Center. Internet publication of these offers a new way of presenting sea ice data, and showing change over time. *(Source: http://www.nsidc.org/news/press/2007_seaiceminimum/20070810_index.html, accessed November 2008)*

Figure 1.13 A bathymetric map, in other words showing underwater depths, of the Arctic region (*Source: http://upload.wikimedia.org/wikipedia/commons/d/d5/ IBCAO_betamap.jpg, accessed November 2008)*

Activity 1.4   Animated maps

Figures 1.14 and 1.15 are still images taken from animated maps. Links to the animations are provided on the course website. Spend about 15 minutes looking at these animations.

The Arctic is a place where maps change with the seasons, as they show changes in sea ice extent in winter and summer. Animations of satellite mappings of sea ice extent over time, such as those in Figures 1.14 and 1.15, can look almost like the planet breathing in and out over the course of an annual cycle. The reductions in the area of summer sea ice in recent years are seen as one of the most tangible expressions of current climate change, and animated maps can show these changes quickly and simply. These mappings are important for climate change science, but they also provide the basis of media stories about the issue. We do not attempt to know the world solely through maps – we also know it through stories, and journalists are some of the most influential storytellers in contemporary society. The next section will take you inside the process of telling news stories about environmental change.

SAQ 1.1   The work that maps do

1   What does the 10 °C isotherm mark?
2   What political and cultural points does a map of Arctic languages demonstrate?
3   Why have bathymetric maps of the Arctic become more politically significant in recent years?
4   Why are animated maps of the extent of summer sea ice important in terms of public understanding of climate change?

Summary of Section 2

In just a few pages this section has shown very different maps of the Arctic, made for a range of purposes. Mercator's highly imaginative map existed to inform some of the first European expeditions to the North, and to summarise both the facts and the myths about the region. The physical, political and language maps help to plot the sometimes conflicting human interests in the region. The bathymetric and satellite image-based maps show the physical forms of the Arctic with a startling degree of accuracy. Furthermore, it is now possible to create animations that show the dynamism of the Arctic environment. In addition to learning about different types of map, you have also been introduced to some of the key conceptual tools in map-making and navigating, including the use of measures of latitude and longitude and the use of different projections.

The Arctic in the media

3

Anyone coming to study the Arctic region in a focused way will be carrying a bundle of ideas and images triggered by the word 'Arctic'. Your answers to Activity 1.1 will have uncovered some of your own. Many of these, particularly the contemporary issues and pictures, will have been planted in your mind by the modern media. The media – TV, newspapers, books and the internet – offer the main ways in which we come to know about places, people and issues beyond our immediate experience. Journalists and other media producers literally 'mediate' between new knowledge, experiences, events and change in the world and the individual consumer of newspapers, broadcasts and so on. They are selecting and translating from a huge body of potential material in ways that shape much of our knowledge of the world beyond our own lives.

> The course DVD contains four video clips in the section 'Arctic in the media'. Now would be a good time to look at these clips, which show how the media report on events in the Arctic.

The internet has softened the boundary between producers and consumers of media messages in some important ways. Unpaid enthusiasts can set up their own web pages or blogs and share their version of world events with potential audiences of millions. Nevertheless, journalists, editors, photographers, camera operators, picture editors and other media professionals continue to shape much of our experience of the world.

Box 1.3   Environment and the media – key ingredients

Environmental issues have provided the media with plenty of strong stories and images. Environmental campaigners (and increasingly, researchers) have long understood the needs of the media. They know that hundreds of stories are vying for attention within the limited space of the news media. News organisations need strong personalities or evidence of an event or change (in other words, 'news'). A story will always have more chance of making it on to a prominent page or place in a broadcast bulletin if it has a strong element of conflict or struggle. With visual media, above all TV news, strong images can sway editorial decisions. This is as true of the Arctic as anywhere else.

Telling environmental change stories (whether about climate change or biodiversity loss) presents challenges to the media. The science and politics are complex and generally slow-moving by news standards and there are few personalities on which to hang stories. There are also large uncertainties: these are stories about physical processes of environmental change caused by both natural processes and billions of human actions and choices. Furthermore, lurking beneath what looks like a story about scientific knowledge can be some very far-reaching ethical and political questions that are difficult to weave into a few hundred words or a two-minute broadcast news story.

To help understand these processes, this section follows the steps through the making of a news story about the Arctic. It explores the origins of the idea for a story, the steps gone through within the news organisation to get the story commissioned, planned, and either captured on film and broadcast or printed in a newspaper and online.

Journalists are always looking for ways to make their stories come to life. The world is awash with media offerings, and the Web opens up a whole world of media material, both professional and amateur. To get a story commissioned, and then to get people to read, listen to or watch it often requires a degree of imagination. At the core of it will be the germ of an idea for a story. Journalists rarely talk about 'issues' as campaigners might, or 'research findings' as academics would. They are in pursuit of great stories.

Some of the best news storytellers work with the BBC, and David Shukman is one of the BBC's leading environment journalists. Figure 1.16 shows him working on a story that illustrates the diverse consequences of climate change in the Arctic (see Figure 1.17). He has made a name for telling strong 'picture stories' from charismatic locations. In other words, he is good at identifying stories that have a strong visual appeal that will help to draw in large audiences who might not otherwise be interested in what appears to be a science story. He has recorded a number of stories from the Antarctic and the Arctic.

Figure 1.16 The BBC's David Shukman in the Arctic, applying the full potential of communications technologies to the challenge of bringing immediacy and interest to stories about climate change *(Source: http://news.bbc.co.uk/1/hi/sci/ tech/7033831.stm, accessed November 2008)*

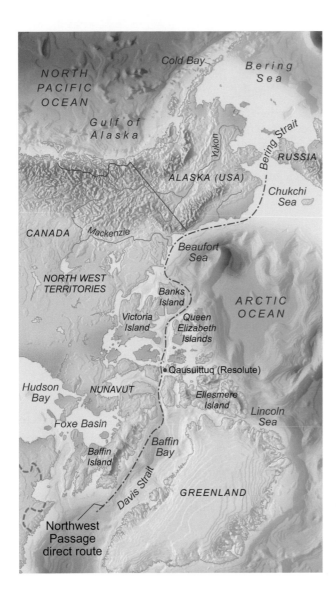

Figure 1.17 Specially commissioned graphics use simple techniques to help audiences to locate and understand the story in just a few seconds (*Source: adapted from http://news.bbc.co.uk/1/hi/sci/tech/7033831.stm, accessed November 2008*)

On each occasion his work has required big investments of money and time by his organisation, so any new proposal has to have very strong justification. Indeed, in the case of the story he discusses in the quote below, the news editors who decide what stories get told had already made it clear that they were not looking for any more 'polar ice melt' or 'polar bears in trouble' stories. I wrote to David to ask about how the story came about and he commented that:

> … while a few years ago I could successfully pitch stories about Greenland's ice retreating or the polar bears being threatened, that threshold has now been raised. Although editors knew the public were interested in climate change stories they felt the polar stories had got clichéd. They wanted some unexpected or dramatic impact from the melting – new geography or new sea routes.

> (*Personal communication with the author, July 2008*)

The opportunity for a striking new story from the Arctic was presented by the historic event of the opening of the Northwest Passage to shipping. It was a challenging story, but a strong one. He writes:

> … the challenges I faced telling the story of the Northwest Passage are even worse than those facing OU students with a tight deadline and limited word count! Broadcast news stories are only a couple of minutes long; they have to be thoroughly researched and accurate, but they also have to be made so that people want to stay with them – with strong pictures, a great location or a gripping story. I knew I had a good story with the Northwest Passage because the chance to navigate it represents a major historic event linked to the climate change issue.

> *(Personal communication with the author, July 2008)*

> To carry out an internet search you need to use a search engine such as Google. To access Google, go into a browser such as Internet Explorer and type www.google.co.uk. In the blank 'search' box on the page that comes up, type in the words that are significant to your search, e.g. 'polar bear ice'. These are usually referred to as keywords. Once you have clicked on 'Google Search' you will be presented with many underlined links that you can click on to access information, articles and images that are related to polar bears and ice.

Activity 1.5   Telling climate change stories

At a convenient moment in the next few days look for a news media article on the Arctic. This activity should take you no more than an hour in total. It will extend some of the thinking you did for Activity 1.2 in Block 1. You might be lucky and find an article in a current periodical or newspaper, but it is more likely that you will need to conduct an internet search. Narrow your search to a particular question that interests you as a result of studying this block – it might be scientific, political or cultural (my example that follows was based on a half-remembered newspaper article. I did an internet search using the keywords 'climate change Greenland Inuit'). Note down how long the piece is (in words or minutes), what images (moving or stills) accompanied it, and why they might have been chosen. Identify how the story's main points were substantiated in terms of reference to reports, or quotes from individuals.

Discussion

I found a story from a British newspaper that showed how climate change was transforming the lives of Inuit Greenlanders, for both better and worse. It was a long features article of around 1600 words – much longer than a news article would normally be. While the number of people hunting was declining rapidly, with consequences for the long-established culture of the Inuit communities, it was also clear that new opportunities were emerging. These centred on the promise of riches for the whole community from selling the rights to extract minerals that are likely to become more accessible with climate changes. The article was illustrated with an engaging photo that helped me identify with the people referred to, and a map that helped to locate it. Whatever the story you considered, and the steps you identified, the activity is likely to have emphasised a few common features of news stories such as pictures, personality, event or change, and conflict or struggle.

The account of the production of the TV news story about the Northwest Passage and your own work with another story gives some sense of how journalists apply hard-won craft skills to the task of communicating environmental issues. In these ways the media can help to translate complex 'issues' into narratives, often with a human interest angle. Their use of strong images, such as in Figure 1.18, can catch the eye and draw new readers and viewers into the story and engage them emotionally.

Figure 1.18 Journalists know that a charismatic species such as the polar bear can help to sell papers: they engage readers emotionally. However, at the same time they are in danger of generating 'climate clichés' (and peddling inaccuracies). *(Source: http://www.thesun.co.uk/sol/homepage/news/article30854. ece, accessed November 2008)*

Global environmental change issues such as climate change and biodiversity loss have been given increasing space in some of the most popular print, television and online media. This has got millions more people thinking and talking about them. However, critiques of the media's performance on environmental issues often focus on some of the negative consequences of some popularisations:

- Seeking out 'human interest' angles can serve to distract people from engaging with the underlying physical processes.
- Persistent use of certain images as a form of shorthand (for example polar bears) can serve to create or underpin clichéd, limited and sometimes false representations of environmental change issues, and induce boredom.
- Some of the attempts to condense complex issues leave the public with a dangerously simplistic notion of, in this case, the Arctic and processes of environmental change.
- Favouring conflict in stories has led to an unbalanced presentation of the science of climate change, wherein the very small number of sceptics (who argue that human-induced climate change is probably not happening) have sometimes been given equal weight with the climate science community (who almost universally believe that it is).

The internet and global environmental change issues have emerged over the same period. The internet has developed into a distinctive new medium that some suggest has the potential to overcome the limitations of other media such as print, radio and television. Its benefits include the facts that:

- searching for specific stories or topics is instant, and browsing across a general theme is also easy
- access to some archived material is straightforward
- users become more than passive readers – audiences can contribute material, dispute claims and generate and share their own material
- the 'barriers to entry' are very low in terms of the costs of publishing your own material on the Web (on websites, blogs, etc).

News media are central players in shaping the extent and quality of public debate about environmental change. The emergence of the internet brings both new storytellers and new ways of telling stories and offering information about the Arctic. However, it is only one kind of communication. Many people have approached the Arctic not as the subject of academic research or of news stories but as a storehouse of the imagination. Artists and writers have long worked to open up a very different set of imaginative responses to the world based on ideas of the far north.

Study note: searching the World Wide Web

The World Wide Web describes all of the publicly accessible websites in the world, in addition to any other information sources that web browsers can access, for example newsgroups. The Web is a useful source of information, but it is quite unlike library catalogues and databases in that it is not so neatly organised. On the Web you can look at information which can be in the form of text, images, video or audio. Websites are linked together using a system called hypertext, which allows you to move from site to site. You use something called a browser, such as Firefox or Internet Explorer, to access this information.

The information itself varies greatly in quality and usefulness. Library catalogues and academic journals are accessible online (but not always free of charge). Increasingly too, the Web is used as a delivery medium for official information like government publications and public records. Timetables and professional directories may also be useful as you develop study and research plans. You can also access bookshops via the Web and buy books and other resources online. Newspapers and magazines online may provide less reliable but nonetheless useful information.

New sources of information are emerging as users start to exploit the capabilities of the Web. In particular there are blogs, personal online weblogs, like online public diaries. You may find useful information on these but you need always to check that it is reliable and accurate and available for re-use. In your time as an Open University student you are likely to use some form of online communication to share your thoughts with others, via a blog or other form of social media.

Whatever you use it for, you need to remember that the Web is a vast and useful resource, but the information you can find there is only as good as the providers make it. Sometimes there will be questions about how accurate or how balanced that information is. You may need to do some further investigations before using the material for your studies.

SAQ 1.2   Media and environment – the downside

This section has made clear the value of media storytelling about environmental issues. But it has also identified some ways in which public understanding of these questions can be limited by the way journalists frame them. Write a short paragraph that summarises these.

Summary of Section 3

Section 3 has introduced you to the ways in which journalists tell stories about environmental change, and in the process shape the ways in which most people come to understand these processes. It has detailed the ways in which broadcast journalism, newspapers and online news use devices to make their stories interesting to readers. But it has also pointed out some of the problems that result from the techniques and practices of journalism. You have also been given some guidance on searching the World Wide Web.

4

Imagining the Arctic

I wanted to go north. I wanted to go to the Arctic. I'd never been to the Arctic – I've never been to the Arctic – but I love the Arctic as a place to think about, to dream about.

Philip Pullman talking about his decision to set much of the action in his book
The Northern Lights in the Arctic (Pullman, 2007)

Almost all of this course is based upon academic research in science, technology and the social sciences. There is a danger, however, that the course might forget to acknowledge the very prominent place that the imagination has in the ways in which humans understand their environments (although it is worth acknowledging the often-forgotten fact that imagination also has an important role in the development of research). Creative and artistic practice is fundamental to the way in which humans engage with some of the biggest questions they face. Hence it is no surprise that some artists and writers have gone to the Arctic (in their imagination or in reality) to engage directly with grand themes concerning humanity's place in the world.

The first book in Philip Pullman's *His Dark Materials* trilogy conjured a world of armoured polar bears (Figure 1.19), secret research laboratories, colonies of witches and remote Nordic trading posts. Much of the action is set in Svalbard (shown in Figure 1.11), a place this block will return to several times. In this case a writer spun threads of research and imagination together to create a complete parallel world. There was something about

Figure 1.19 The Armoured Bears that feature in the National Theatre production of Philip Pullman's *His Dark Materials*, the first part of which was also made into a film, *The Golden Compass*

this distant place that made it seem a natural host to his remarkable story. Although the author provides some of the essential components, his readers go on to do their own work with the narrative, creating their own pictures and importing their own ideas and experiences of the Arctic in the process. The region holds a powerful place in our imagination even though – or perhaps because – so few people have been there. It is, in the author's words, a great place to 'to think about, to dream about'.

As with any human representations of the natural world, art inspired by the Arctic serves different cultural and imaginative purposes at different times. For the nineteenth-century Romantic movement of writers and painters (see Figure 1.20) such distant wilderness landscapes offered a setting in which to explore themes of spirituality, mortality and the sublime in nature.

Figure 1.20 German Romantic painter Caspar David Friedrich's *The Polar Sea* **or** *The Wreck of Hope*, **1824**

The Arctic and subarctic regions still work on people in many different ways, and few visitors return unaffected. The Canadian pianist and documentary maker Glenn Gould (Figure 1.21) made an experimental radio documentary series that tried to distil what it is about 'The Idea of North' that is so powerful. You can find clips from Glenn Gould's radio documentary online if you are interested. One of the intriguing things about it is the way he laid extracts of interviews one on top of another, creating a soundscape out of the different voices – almost a choir. Some describe this work as a sound poem. One of the things this suggested to me is the diversity of ideas that people have of the same thing or place; it reminds us that there is not just one definition of 'the environment', but rather many accounts of many environments.

Box 1.4   Pianist Glenn Gould's 'Idea of North'

Figure 1.21 Glenn Gould wanted to explore the hold that the world's northern regions had on both his own and the collective imagination in his experimental documentaries

When I went to the North, I had no intention of writing about or of referring to it… in anything that I wrote. And yet, almost despite myself, I began to draw all sorts of metaphorical allusions based on what was really a very limited knowledge of the country and a very casual exposure to it. I found myself writing musical critiques, for instance, in which the idea of the North began to serve as a foil for other ideas and values that seemed to me depressingly urban oriented and spiritually limited thereby… I'm by no means alone in this reaction to the North; there are very few people who make contact with it and emerge entirely unscathed. Something really does happen to most people who go into the North – they become at least aware of the creative opportunity which the physical fact of the country represents and – quite often, I think – come to measure their own work and life against that rather staggering creative possibility: they become, in effect, philosophers.

(Transcript from Glenn Gould's Canadian Broadcasting Corporation experimental radio documentary The Idea of North)

Going back to Activity 1.1, it is likely that you referred to wilderness, wide open space, 'cold deserts', and other accounts of a place that contrasts strongly with the dense, urban or suburban places that most people on the planet now inhabit. Perhaps it is this contrast that makes the Arctic such a powerful place in the imagination of many people from further south. Climate change has given a new energy to the imaginative work that people engage in related to the Arctic.

Box 1.5   Cape Farewell: art explores climate

The Cape Farewell project was initiated by the artist David Buckland. In addition to being a photographic artist he is also an experienced sailor. These two aspects of his life came together as he began to learn about the changes that oceanographers were beginning to identify as a result of climate change. He had strong instincts that this was an issue that should not be left in the hands of scientists and policy people alone, but that artists, writers and musicians should engage directly with the issue. The Cape Farewell project took shape as a series of voyages in the Arctic region in a sailing vessel, the *Noorderlicht* (meaning 'northern lights' in Dutch; see Figure 1.22). The crews have been made up of scientists and creative people, including world-famous names from the arts. Some of the material inspired by the voyages has made its way into broadcast and online material, publications and art exhibitions. Some have embarked on the expeditions with the aim of finding ways of communicating scientific knowledge of climate change in new ways. Others view it as an opportunity to extend thinking beyond the scientific facts or policy proposals to invite people who experience their work to join them on imaginative and ethical journeys.

Figure 1.22 One of the most prominent examples of the arts engaging with environmental issues is the Cape Farewell project, which has led expeditions to the Arctic aboard the sailing vessel *Noorderlicht*

Activity 1.6   Investigating online materials

To complement your reading of this chapter you could take no more than an hour to explore some of the creative material referred to in this section and linked to on the course website. When next online you can listen to an excerpt from Glenn Gould's documentary 'The Idea of North' and you could browse the archives and current work of the Cape Farewell project. Links are provided on the course website.

Figure 1.23 Choreographer Siobhan Davies' response to her trip to the Arctic with a Cape Farewell expedition was the installation *Endangered Species*, appearing here in Liverpool Cathedral

Figure 1.24 Detail from Siobhan Davies' *Endangered Species*

The choreographer Siobhan Davies wanted to create a performance that would bring together the primal emotions and rational thoughts that her journey to the Arctic had evoked. Working with a dancer and a fashion designer she created a film of a dance which was then projected inside a cabinet, appearing like a hologram. The cabinet resembles a museum display case (Figure 1.23), and she titled the work *Endangered Species*. The viewer sees a small, semi-human figure dancing gracefully inside the case, her movements exaggerated by a costume of long, bending rods that increase in number as her dance progresses (Figure 1.24). While at first they liberate her by extending the boundaries of her body, the many rods eventually restrict and finally extinguish her small life form. As with many artists, Siobhan Davies does not want to make the work or the message very explicit, but is prompting viewers both to think about the endangered state of humanity and also provoking them into a powerful emotional reaction. The artwork prompted in me thoughts about the burdens and complexities of contemporary living. I walked away asking myself the questions: 'Are our highly polluting modern lives really delivering a good quality of life? How can we strip things down a little and look for more *quality* above quantity?'

Peter Clegg has long made environmental considerations central to his work. He joined the expedition of artists and scientists in order to better understand the realities of climate change. Architects spend much of their time considering the dimensions of things, and sensitivity to space is central to their work. Before he travelled to the Arctic he made some calculations that would help to express CO_2 in terms of a volume rather than a weight, because he felt it was easier to make sense of. Clegg's thinking is spelled out in his own words in Box 1.6. He worked with artist Antony Gormley to create a sculptural statement that would help people to connect the difficult idea of CO_2 emissions per head of population and their environmental consequences. They created three related sculptures by carving ice and snow, based on Peter Clegg's calculations (Figure 1.25).

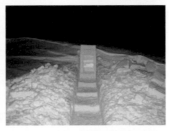

Figure 1.25 Antony Gormley and Peter Clegg, _Three Made Places_, 2005. This series of photographs shows the artwork _Three Made Places_, which comprises _Shelter_, _Standing Room_ and _Block_. It was made by the architect Peter Clegg and the sculptor Antony Gormley during the Cape Farewell expedition of artists and scientists to the Svalbard. The work tries to express an individual human's CO_2 emissions in sculptural form and helps to connect the discussions in the last two parts of Block 1 with the material you consider in Block 2.

Box 1.6   An architect imagines CO_2

We know that the major culprit is manmade carbon dioxide emissions and we are becoming aware of the concept of a kilogram of carbon dioxide as a measurement of global pollution from cars and buildings. But what do we understand by a kilogram of CO_2? How can our minds grasp the weight of a gas? We understand a gallon of petrol, a pint of beer, a pound of sugar more because we see them as volumes than feel them as weight. Some time ago it occurred to me that it might be helpful to try to define the kilogram of CO_2 as a space rather than mass. One kilogram of CO_2 at atmospheric pressure occupies 0.54 of a cubic metre.

That is the volume, approximately, taken up by ourselves and the space immediately around us – it is roughly the volume occupied by a coffin, which is perhaps an appropriate symbolic unit when we are talking about the destruction of the planet. Once we have this image in our minds we can then start to relate that 'coffin's worth' of CO_2... to the emissions resulting from leaving on a 100 watt tungsten electric light bulb for a day... We can look at a pound of strawberries from Israel and recognise that it costs us and the world that same coffin's worth of CO_2 to bring it to London... In the UK each one of us is responsible for nearly 10,000 coffins [of CO_2] and America is responsible for 20,000. In a sustainable future our emissions should be less than 2,000 coffins per year.

(Clegg, 2005)

SAQ 1.3   Imagining CO_2

1   How many coffins' worth of CO_2 would you be responsible for if you drove an average petrol car 20 miles (32 km) per day for 225 days during a year, if the emissions of the car were 0.2 kg CO_2 per km?

2   Look back at Table 3.2 in Part 3 of Block 1.

How many coffins' worth of CO_2 would you save per year if you replaced ten 60 watt incandescent light bulbs with ten 11 watt energy-saving lamps?

The explorations you have considered in the sections on the media and arts have been undertaken with the goal of enabling better understanding of or engagement with the Arctic or environmental change. However, most historic exploration of the region has been undertaken with different kinds of reward in mind – whether it be personal or national wealth, or celebrity. The final section of Part 1 considers nearly five centuries of attempts to 'claim' the Arctic.

Summary of Section 4

This section has introduced a number of different forms of artistic response to the environment and processes of change in the Arctic. It has shown the ways in which the Arctic is a powerful stimulus to the imagination – even for people who have never been there. It has shown that it is rewarding to complement scientific or geographic representations of the Arctic environment with insights drawn from writing, photography, painting, music and sculpture. The section showed how it can be a place that inspires.

Claiming the Arctic

5

The Arctic is an intriguing place to think about issues of sovereignty; that is, who lays claim to 'own' a piece of land and what are the origins of that claim.

It is easy to think of the exploration and exploitation of the Arctic by western societies as a relatively recent phenomenon. When I first thought about Arctic exploration by Europeans I conjured images of black-and-white photos of men, dogs and sleds racing to be first to the poles. In fact, the history of exploration and exploitation of the Arctic dates back much earlier. It is known that Vikings settled on Greenland in the tenth century, and Greenland is still a (self-governing) region of Denmark today, although in late 2008 it voted for greater independence. But the history of exploration as it is understood in the modern sense of map-making and claiming territory starts in the sixteenth-century expedition by the English adventurer Martin Frobisher.

A combination of technological, economic and political developments combined to see the major European powers competing to explore and claim 'new' territories. You may recall that Mercator thought that the islands near the North Pole were habitable. Furthermore, European thinkers thought the Arctic to be potentially rich in natural resources. In 1580 John Dee (Figure 1.26), one of the major intellectual figures of his era in Europe, drafted a case for the English Queen Elizabeth's sovereignty over the Arctic. This was in part based on recent expeditions that Dee had helped to plan, but also on a fanciful historical claim. Dee suggested that the British King Arthur had 'not only conquered Iseland, Groenland, and all the Northern Iles compassing unto Russia, But even unto the North Pole … did extend his Jurisdiction: And sent Colonies thither' (McGhee, 2005, p. 28). Dee was the first to use the phrase 'British empire' and his designs on the Arctic were just one element of a project of expansion of Elizabeth's realm.

Three Elizabethan expeditions to the Arctic were led by Martin Frobisher (Figure 1.27), an explorer and privateer, or pirate. Frobisher was searching for a route 'to the West Sea, whereby to pas to Cathay and to the East India.' In other words, they were looking for a north-west passage to the north of the Americas that would open up a route to the riches of the east but would avoid navigating waters controlled by their arch-enemy, Spain. They failed in this attempt, succeeding only in mapping areas of north-western Canada. However, investigating the reasons for, and accounts of, these expeditions helps introduce themes of great relevance today.

The 'western' imagination, meaning European and American culture, has pictured the Arctic as an empty wilderness, available to be annexed. However, the first European explorers had very different expectations of the place: they were optimistic about the Arctic's capacity to support a European way of life. They were a long way from home, and as they

Figure 1.26 John Dee, mathematician, geographer, astrologer, and adviser to Elizabeth I, was the first to coin the term 'British empire', and argued that the Arctic should be claimed by the English Queen

Figure 1.27 Martin Frobisher: an unlikely Arctic explorer? The adventurer laid claim to the Arctic for Queen Elizabeth I, while seeking gold and a north-west passage to China and the Indies.

looked out over the treeless summer landscape of Baffin Island they found parallels with the deforested highlands of Yorkshire and Scotland. Hence, before their return voyage in 1578 they 'sowed pease, corne, and other graine, to prove the fruitfulnesse of the soyle against the next yeare' (Frobisher's publisher, George Best, quoted in McGhee, 2005, p. 159).

This was not the only false assumption they made. Frobisher had assumed the Arctic to be uninhabited, but in August 1576 climbed to the top of a hill on Baffin Island and:

> … being ashore, upon the toppe of a hill, he perceived a number of small things fleeting in the Sea a farre off, whyche hee supposed to be Porposes, or Ceales, or some kinde of strange fishe: but coming nearer, he discovered them to be men, in small boates made of leather.

> *(Narrative of Frobisher's voyage, published by George Best, quoted in McGhee, 2005, p. 102 (Figure 1.28))*

Figure 1.28 Appearing in George Best's account of one of Frobisher's expeditions, and probably based on the appearance of Inuit hostages who were taken to Bristol in 1577, this inventive picture includes European-style tents

Frobisher's sixteenth-century expeditions were enormously expensive and required wealthy sponsors willing to take substantial risks. Both adventurers such as Frobisher and his sponsors were driven above all by the lure of material reward. The profits in this case lay in the promise of opening a new sea route, and also in the discovery of gold deposits. Despite failing in their purpose of discovering a north-west passage his expeditions did bring back very large quantities of what he thought to be gold ore. An enormous smelting works – thought to be the largest in England at that time – was created in Dartford, Kent, purely to extract the gold from the ore. When it became clear that this 'ore' was no more than a valueless hard, black stone it was used instead to build what must have been the most expensive manor house wall on the planet (Figure 1.29).

The search for a north-west passage continued in the nineteenth century. The most famous attempt was undertaken by Sir John Franklin, a veteran of Nelson's naval campaigns and a gifted navigator. He made a detailed

Figure 1.29 The final resting place of Frobisher's 'gold ore', still visible in an Elizabethan manor house wall in Dartford, Kent, UK

record of his 1819–22 expedition to the Canadian Arctic. His account of the extraordinary dangers and demands made upon western explorers shows how highly they prized an understanding of, and claim over, the high Arctic. Franklin concluded that:

> Our researches, as far as they have gone, favour the opinion of those who contend for the practicability of a North-West Passage. The general line of coast probably runs east and west, nearly in the latitude assigned to Mackenzie's River… and I think there is little doubt of a continued sea, in or about that line of direction. The existence of whales too, on this part of the coast, evidenced by the whalebone we found in Esquimaux Cove, may be considered as an argument for an open sea; and a connexion with Hudson's Bay is rendered more probable from the same kind of fish abounding on the coasts we visited, and on those to the north of Churchill River.
>
> *(Franklin, 1998, p. 383)*

Franklin died, along with all of his crew, in 1847 (Figure 1.30). It took a number of search expeditions before their remains were found, along with

Figure 1.30 Cairn erected over the grave of members of the Franklin expedition in Douglas Bay, King William Land

evidence that Franklin had been the first European explorer in 250 years of searching to discover the fabled Northwest Passage. Although it was permanently sealed with ice at the time, you know from David Shukman's news story in Section 1 about the Northwest Passage that, as a result of climate change, this is no longer the case year round.

The British were not the only ones with an extensive history of exploration in the Arctic. The Norwegian cartoon in Figure 1.31 reflects their own engagement with the region. The cartoon celebrates the explorer Amundsen's extraordinary achievement of being the first person to reach the South Pole and the first person to explore both poles. It is represented as a national as much as a personal achievement and comes from the 'golden age' of polar exploration at the end of the nineteenth century and the beginning of the twentieth. The image nicely captures the 'heroic' period of nationalist exploration of the late nineteenth and early twentieth centuries.

More recently the Arctic has prompted thinking about new issues concerning who might claim resources that have been made newly accessible by the physical transformations brought about by climate change. Another way of phrasing this is to ask who has sovereignty over a place.

Figure 1.31 In 1919 this Norwegian cartoonist celebrates his countrymen being the first to arrive at both poles, with the caption: The English have a lot, to be sure, but we Norwegians have more ice!

Box 1.7   Sovereignty

Political maps such as that in Figure 1.11 suggest to the reader that nation states are tidy 'containers' of political life. This way of thinking has its roots in the Peace of Westphalia of 1648, when, after the very destructive Thirty Years War, Europe's monarchies agreed to recognise each other's right to rule their own territories without interference from neighbouring sovereign powers. This agreement can be considered the source of all modern international law, and sovereignty can be defined as an exclusive right to have control over a territory and people. The French Revolution saw a shift in thinking about who holds sovereign power, moving it away from a sovereign being, with authority derived from a notion of divine or God-given right, towards the population of a nation state – the citizenry. You will recall from the discussion of the state in Block 1 that state institutions enjoy the legitimate authority to set and raise taxes and make and enforce laws, and they control the police and the army within their borders.

This way of thinking came to dominate the whole globe only in the twentieth century, as global empires collapsed. Statehood and national self-determination became the primary principles by which the people of the world came to be organised politically. The creation of the United Nations (UN) both responded to and confirmed the spread of this system across the globe, with almost all nations belonging to it. Within the UN system the principles of nation state sovereignty, liberty and democracy come together to form the dominant ideals, and in many cases the organising features, of modern political life.

Indigenous peoples whose land had been colonised in preceding centuries (above all by Europeans) did not fit into this system. Before colonisation these people had lived outside what Europeans recognised as the boundaries of political community. They had no comparable structures of government, or record of their inhabitation. More significant, perhaps, they had only modest power or organisation with which to resist the technologies (including weapons) of the European colonists. For these and other reasons indigenous peoples, whether in Australia, the Arctic or South America, were seen as living beyond the norms and principles of European societies. They therefore presented no obstacle to a colonial claim. In the last three decades of the twentieth century indigenous peoples campaigned for new legal settlements and rights. In the Arctic this is reflected in the formation of the Inuit Circumpolar Council.

Global environmental issues pose big questions about the adequacy of the principle of national sovereignty. The consequences of an action in one place (for example carbon emissions in present-day UK or USA) are felt by people distant in space or time (for example the people of the Bangladesh delta threatened by floods, or sub-Saharan Africa affected by drought). It is now recognised that the population of the planet shares just one climate system and one biosphere. This raises important and difficult new questions about where to set the boundaries of political community and ethical responsibility.

Study note: making spray diagrams

Another way of making notes is to use the technique of *spray diagrams*. This is a way of organising knowledge that encourages you to show the links between ideas. There are various terms used to describe the resulting diagram – spider diagrams, pattern notes or 'mind maps', but the principles are similar. The techniques used to draw these kinds of notes are also useful when planning longer pieces of writing such as essays.

This is how to make a spray diagram of the first paragraph of Box 1.7. On a piece of paper write the main theme or question in the centre of the page – in this case the definition of 'sovereignty'. Then a circle (or box) is drawn around this text. This becomes the 'hub' of the spray diagram. A line is then drawn from the hub to the next fact or idea: in this case the origins of sovereignty. This becomes a node on the spray diagram. A box or circle is drawn around the new text. Additional information that explains or adds detail to this node can be added. In this example the Treaty of Westphalia is cited as the origin of the modern concept of sovereignty, but the author says that the original idea of sovereignty was modified by the ideas behind the French Revolution. All these steps can be repeated to add new nodes and supporting detail, and if diagrams are being drawn for personal use it may not be necessary to use boxes or circles for key points.

You can watch a demonstration of making a spray diagram by following the link on the course website.

SAQ 1.4   Making notes as a spray diagram

Figure 1.32 shows an incomplete spray diagram using the information from Box 1.7.

Complete the spray diagram, adding your own notes to nodes 2 and 3 titled Powers and Problems.

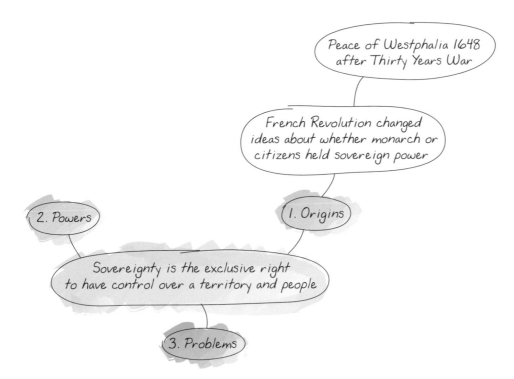

Figure 1.32 **Incomplete spray diagram**

Although the race to the poles had little strategic significance, in the same period there had been competition to claim minerals rights. Svalbard has been the site of coal mining since the late nineteenth century, culminating in a 'coal rush' between competing American, Norwegian, British, Russian, Swedish and Dutch companies, which were in several cases being actively encouraged by their national governments (Figure 1.33). In the early twenty-first century companies and nation states have again begun to jostle over claims to Arctic mineral resources (and now newly opened sea routes).

Figure 1.33 **The Arctic Coal Company staff house on Svalbard with the mine visible higher up the hillside. The American owner John M. Longyear gave his name to what is now the capital of Svalbard, Longyearben.**

Figure 1.34 Artist Alex Hartley claims sovereignty over the newly revealed island 'Nymark' in 2005

The Norwegian cartoon in Figure 1.31 and the photo of a mountaineer in Figure 1.34 have been made with very different intentions in mind, but they share a distinctive pose.

Figure 1.34 shows the artist and mountaineer Alex Hartley, pictured during the 2004 Cape Farewell expedition. The photo marks the moment when he claimed for himself sovereignty of a previously unseen and unmapped island that he came across on the voyage. Although his approach is tongue in cheek the intentions are very serious. The island had been revealed by a retreating glacier, the melting of which has been accelerated by climate change. One of Hartley's prime aims was to draw attention to the impacts of climate change through the artwork he made by mapping and claiming the land. Among other things, his ironic work invites people to reflect on the fact that as the ice retreats there will be sovereignty battles around access to fossil fuel resources. The island he dubbed Nymark (translated from Norwegian as 'new ground' or 'uncharted territory') provides an entertaining and insightful case. Hartley has some plans for his new island:

> We surveyed the island taking longitude and latitude readings for all features and extremities. A cairn was built and in the age-old style, a claim note was placed inside a tin-can and this in turn was inserted into the cairn. The note stated, in both English and Norwegian, notice of our claim on the newly revealed land. Upon our return to the mainland, our new island will be charted and I will submit it for inclusion in all subsequent maps. The land will be named and registered.

> Nothing has yet been ruled out; annexation, independence, tax haven, wildlife sanctuary, short-let holiday homes or time-shares. Postcards will be printed and a major architectural competition will be launched. Engineers will be consulted as to how best to keep all the mud together and prevent any shrinkage of our island.

(Hartley, 2005)

In Figure 1.34 Hartley poses at the summit of Nymark. Behind him the sailing boat that carried him and a mix of scientists and other artists on the Cape Farewell expedition can be seen. The pose and the design of the image draws upon portraits of explorers and adventurers of Europe's colonising past, and echoes the pose of the Norwegian explorers in the cartoon in Figure 1.31. The image is put together in such a way as to suggest in the viewer's mind the long history of European exploration of 'new' lands. These historic explorers were, more often than not, pursuing new territories to claim for the empire or nation to which they belonged, or had been hired by. Their expeditions might have a number of new purposes: mapping new territory; capturing or cataloguing new species; researching available resources. However, one of the prime purposes has always been the claiming and naming of new lands, and most of the activities of the explorers have been driven by the promise of economic and political benefit.

Hartley's artwork, shown in its exhibited form in Figures 1.35 and 1.36, provokes in my mind thoughts about far more serious cases of sovereignty

Figure 1.35 Alex Hartley's installation in the Art of Climate Change exhibition, called *Nymark (Undiscovered Island) 2005–2006*. It is a collage including photos, maps and letters to and from the Norwegian government relating to his claim of Nymark.

conflicts in the region. Minerals, including fossil fuels formed over the long sweep of geological time, are likely to become more easily accessible. This is because the burning of fossil fuels and consequent rise in temperatures is making exploration for, and extraction of, fossil fuels easier in the Arctic.

Figure 1.36 Alex Hartley, *Nymark (Undiscovered Island) 2005–2006* (detail)

However, there is no ironic intent in the planting of a Russian flag using a submarine at the North Pole as shown in Figure 1.37. Some experts dismissed this act as an empty piece of propaganda for the benefit of the Russian electorate, with no significance in international law. Nevertheless, the incident nicely summarises the increasing tension around sovereignty and resources in the Arctic at a time when higher temperatures brought about by climate change promise to make it easier to locate and extract fossil fuels and other resources in the region. Although it may be decades before the extraction of fossil fuels becomes economically viable, news headline writers have been quick to suggest the start of an 'Arctic Cold War'.

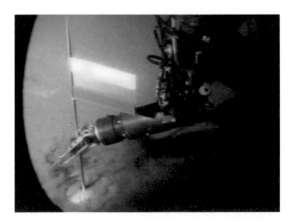

Figure 1.37 The then President Putin of Russia was quoted as saying that 'I am proud our country remains the leader in conquering the Arctic' in Russian local press on the occasion of a flag being placed by mini-submarine at the North Pole

The United States Geological Survey (USGS) published a 'resource appraisal' of the Arctic region in 2008 that made clear why there is increasing tension around the question of who has the right to exploit the mineral deposits in the region. The map in Figure 1.38 shows potential oil and gas resources. It is a complex map, so do not try to analyse it in great detail. A couple of minutes spent studying it will give you the most important information. The survey estimates that the region holds 90 billion barrels of oil (Bird et al., 2008, p. 4). The picture for gas resources is similar: it is thought that there may be as much undiscovered gas as all the reserves known in Russia. The USGS estimate that '[t]he extensive Arctic continental shelves may constitute the geographically largest unexplored prospective area for petroleum remaining on earth' (Bird et al., 2008, p. 1). It is worth noting that press reports also quoted independent analysts who pointed out

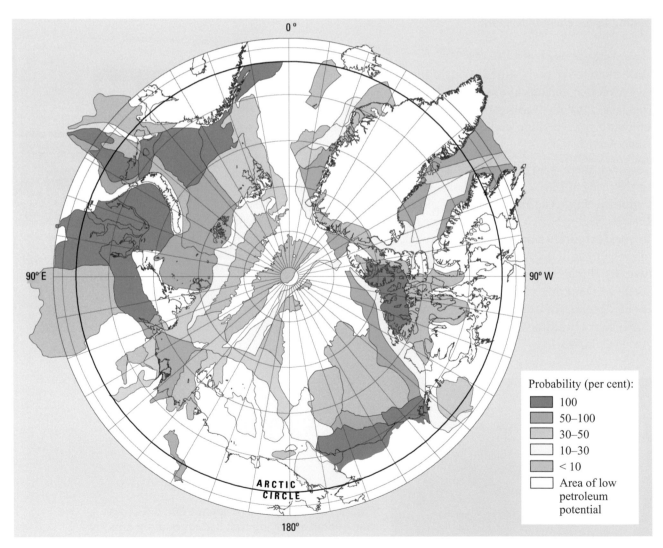

Figure 1.38 A survey of potential oil and gas resources by the US Geological Survey published in 2008 shows significant untapped mineral wealth. These resources will become more easily accessible as temperatures rise.

that there are more easily accessible potential resources around the world, and that the USGS has a tendency to publish optimistic accounts. But the fact remains that all countries of the polar region have a sharpened interest in how sovereignty claims and access to resources will play out in the coming decades as climate change renders more of the mineral resources of the Arctic reachable.

Tensions around sovereignty are also evident between long-time allies Canada and the US. They dispute who has sovereignty over the Northwest Passage: with higher temperatures this could become an important route for sea traffic and hold wider strategic significance.

Nation states in the region have been investing in new research into the Earth's surface under the sea in the hope of reinforcing claims to sovereignty. If countries can clearly demonstrate that their continental mass extends under the sea into the Arctic's potentially resource-rich areas, then they can make stronger sovereignty claims. Hence bathymetric maps such as the one shown in Figure 1.13 have been taking on much greater significance.

How can conflicting claims to sovereignty be resolved? International talks over recent decades have developed the United Nations Convention on the Law of the Sea. The governments of almost all maritime countries have ratified it since the wording was first agreed in 1982 (ratified means confirmed in national legislatures/parliaments). The US government was still resisting ratifying the law at the time of writing in late 2008. But senior figures in government felt that ratification would benefit the US economy because of the opportunity to extend sovereignty claims in the Arctic. John D. Negroponte, then US deputy secretary of state, felt that:

> The United States would also receive direct economic benefit... Specifically, the convention recognizes the sovereign rights of coastal nations over natural resources like oil, gas and minerals, in 'exclusive economic zones' out to 200 nautical miles, and in rigorously defined continental shelf regions. The United States stands to gain considerably, since its Arctic shelf could potentially extend out to 600 nautical miles.

(America.gov, 2007)

Environmental campaigners enter the debate to protect the interests of the flora and fauna of the Arctic. They argue that a very different legal approach is needed to protect the Arctic environment, similar to the Antarctic Treaty of 1961, which bans the exploitation of natural resources in that region. But that approach is also in danger of forgetting communities with an even greater interest in the future of the region.

SAQ 1.5   Maps, climate change and sovereignty

How do bathymetric maps, climate change and questions of sovereignty interact?

5.1 Whose Arctic is it anyway?

The long history of exploration and exploitation of the Arctic has been framed in this section as a question of sovereignty. But the discussion so far has neglected to consider some of the most important stakeholders in the region: the indigenous peoples. This discussion of sovereignty would be incomplete without analysis of the indigenous Arctic peoples' experience of land and resource claims in the Arctic.

The bravery of Frobisher, Franklin and the other pioneers of polar exploration is startling. It is immensely difficult to place yourself in their position – with poor equipment, very limited supplies and even more limited knowledge of the terrain they were exploring. Even considering the assistance they frequently enjoyed from indigenous Arctic communities their feats are extraordinary. Similarly, the ingenuity of engineers and others in assessing and working out ways of exploiting the Arctic's resources is impressive. Nevertheless, these individuals are representative of a colonialist way of thinking that has dominated the 'view from the South' for centuries. They (we?) thought of this as empty terrain, open to claims. The negative consequences of this way of thinking for the Inuit peoples of the Arctic have been felt in numerous ways, and continue today. Disturbing events in the 1950s confirm that the western imagination about indigenous Arctic people had progressed remarkably little over four centuries.

In 1953 the Canadian government was concerned that US military interests in the Arctic archipelago would see them lose their claim to an unoccupied territory. International law would accept 'effective occupation' and hence the government looked for ways of establishing communities there. The solution came in the forced relocation of Inuit families.

The officials making this decision ignored the fact that the islands to which the Inuit people were sent would never have – indeed could never have – supported a permanent Inuit community. One settlement was named Resolute by the government but was known by the Inuit as Qausuittuq, 'the place with no dawn', suggesting what the unwilling inhabitants thought of the place. It remains the second most northerly settlement in Canada. The decision on the relocations was in part informed by the inaccurate account of Inuit origins and culture developed by western archaeologists and anthropologists, whose work had promoted the notion that 'the Eskimo' were a people uniquely well adapted to the Arctic environment (note that Part 4 mostly focuses on the Inuit experience of the Arctic, and will include a discussion of the different terms used to describe indigenous Arctic peoples). There was evidence of ancient settlements, but these were in fact temporary hunting camps.

The Canadian government officials also claimed that the move served to protect Inuit culture from contamination by contact with European settlements. Similar relocations were undertaken by Danish, Soviet and US governments in defence of sovereignty claims, but the Canadian remains the most dramatic. In the words of the Canadian archaeologist Robert McGhee, who has researched the story, it:

> involved the movement of small groups of families over 1,500 kilometres to the north of their productive Subarctic homeland, into a barren High Arctic environment of intense winter cold and prolonged winter darkness that they had never previously experienced.

(McGhee, 2005, p. 109)

The hamlet of Qausuittuq now has a little over 200 inhabitants, and its own Inuit cooperatively owned hotel that serves as a base for numerous expeditions to the North Pole (1000 km to the north) and wildlife tours. As Figure 1.39 shows, despite the challenges of living in the far north of Canada, there are plenty of things that people would recognise from growing up in the temperate south.

Figure 1.39 Summer in Qausuittuq. The Inuit community descended from the people who experienced the enforced resettlements of the 1950s share the same harsh conditions, but have gained more political and cultural power.

The period since the enforced resettlements has seen positive change for the Inuit in relation to restoration of their culture and the forging of some new forms of sovereignty. Legal action and campaigns have started to reverse the effects of what was in essence a colonisation. One central aim has been to overturn the notion that people would have no legal claim to land in which their antecedents had lived for perhaps a thousand years, simply because their culture lacked 'western' forms of land ownership or historical archives detailing them.

In tandem with new political forces of the last quarter of the twentieth century the Inuit began to assert their rights and interests. From around 1975 Inuit interests became more influential in Canadian politics. This was

Figure 1.40 Nunavut flag. The creation of the first new Canadian territory since 1949, carved out of the North-West Territories, is a tangible expression of a self-confident expression of Inuit culture.

one of the prominent factors in the creation on 1 April 1999 of Nunavut – the territory formed out of a large portion of Canada's North-West Territories. Nearly 25 000 of the just under 30 000 inhabitants are Inuit.

The pile of stones, or inuksuk, which appears on the Nunavut flag (Figure 1.40) is not a marker of a territorial claim or a memorial, but rather an Inuit waymarker. Thus it has some similarities with cairns found in mountain regions, for example in Scotland. Such stone monuments guide people on the land and also indicate sacred and other special places. In a comparatively sparse landscape they are a culturally resonant symbol. The star is the Niqirtsuituq (pronounced nee-RIRT-soo-ee-took), the North Star – the traditional guide for navigation. The North Star also symbolises leadership by the elders of the community.

The creation of the Nunavut territory and its flag are measures of how, over the course of 25 years, the Inuit communities of the polar regions have won back a degree of self-determination and cultural strength. Over the same period the international environmental science community has developed an understanding of climate change, pollutant movements through water and air, and biodiversity loss. These environmental changes introduce new threats to the culture of the indigenous peoples of the Arctic.

Figure 1.41 An Inuit woman prepares a polar bear skin to be made into clothing. The Inuit's relationship with the polar bear is an intimate one, spanning practical and cultural significance. Climate change threatens this culture and way of life.

Activity 1.7   What does a polar bear mean?

Take a close look at the images in Figures 1.41 and 1.42. Think about the different ways in which the subjects of the photos are thinking about polar bears. Note down your thoughts about what the value of polar bears is to the cultures within which the subjects of the photos live

Discussion

In Figure 1.41 an Inuit woman is cleaning and preparing a polar bear skin. There's not much doubt about her doing a job of work with this skin. It is a valuable resource and is going to serve a practical purpose: she is literally sinking her teeth into the task of processing this part of the animal. In Figure 1.42 the environmental activist dressed up in a polar bear suit at a music festival in East Anglia in the UK is drawing on the very different significance of the animal for young Europeans. The campaigner is seeking to draw attention to the threat that climate change poses to the habitat of the polar bear, but in so doing brings to life the effects of the apparently intangible idea that is human-induced climate change. These campaigners have made polar bears the (now clichéd) 'poster children' of climate change. The media have picked up on this visual shorthand for climate change impacts. For me these two photos demonstrate that not only the polar bear but also the whole Arctic region hold very different meanings depending on where you are situated.

Figure 1.42 Environmental NGOs also lay claim to the Arctic. Here a young environmental campaigner at a music festival in East Anglia, UK, wants to provoke concern about climate change.

The climate-change risks faced by Arctic communities are seen as harbingers of changes that threaten all of humanity. In 2005 Sheila Watt-Cloutier, at the time the elected chair of the Inuit Circumpolar Conference, argued on a visit to Britain that 'our land is changing: soon yours will too' and that the Arctic is a 'health barometer for the planet'. She argued that Inuit elders and hunters were reporting changes including:

> melting permafrost causing increased erosion and damaging infrastructure; longer sea-ice free seasons; new species of birds and fish invading the region; the arrival of mosquitoes and black flies; unpredictable sea-ice conditions; and glaciers melting fast, creating torrents instead of streams.

(Watt-Cloutier, 2005)

Watt-Cloutier was only half joking when she summarised the case as being driven by her community's 'right to be cold'.

Debates about rights and responsibilities in relation to climate change have followed fast in the wake of the maturing science. One unusual but revealing example of this is a symposium based on a boat in the Arctic convened by His All Holiness Bartholomew, the spiritual leader of the Orthodox churches' 300 million members (Figure 1.43). Despite holding a post that stretches back to the sixth century, he has led debates amongst faith communities concerning the pressing contemporary issue of climate change. All of the religious leaders attending signed The Icefjord Commitment statement that included these words:

> Amidst the wisdom and majesty of water, ice and sunlight, we have each prayed within the realm of our own traditions. ... We recognise the interdependence of all life, that in its many manifestations sustains this planet,

and realise our dependence on this myriad of relationships… The Earth is a living entity with incredible healing powers, and we have much to learn. It is the task of our generation to leave this sacred Earth, in all its wisdom and beauty to the generations to come. Let the work begin.

(Religion, Science and the Environment, 2007)

Figure 1.43   In September 2007 religious leaders gathered amongst the icebergs and melting glacier at the mouth of the Ilulissat Icefjord in Greenland to learn about climate change and to share in a silent prayer for the Earth

Whatever your beliefs, these excerpts from the Icefjord Commitment are likely to provoke thought about the interdependent relationships among and between humanity and the non-human natural world. They place humans in a much more modest position on the planet than some of the explorers and exploiters that featured in this part. In studying the remainder of the course you should keep in mind the proposition that humanity 'has much to learn'! Responding to the challenge to 'let the work begin' will require that people first equip themselves with a deeper understanding of underlying environmental processes. The next two parts concentrate on the scientific practice that underlies current concern with environmental change. The final part will return to themes of learning and responsibility.

Summary of Section 5

This section has sketched the history of exploration and exploitation of the Arctic region across several centuries, from the sixteenth century to the present. It has explored the significance of the concept of sovereignty for making sense of who has legal claim to control access to resources. You have engaged with the significance of climate change for issues of both exploitation and sovereignty in the present and future. The increasing political and cultural power of indigenous Arctic peoples was introduced, and issues of rights raised by the emergence of evidence of climate change were discussed.

Summary of Part 1

Part 1 introduced you to different ways of knowing about the Arctic. After an introduction, Section 2 introduced different ways of representing the Arctic and the wider world in the form of maps. This section served to orient your study of the Arctic. But it also equipped you to understand some of the core challenges, concepts and techniques of map-making in general. Section 3 explored the ways in which news media represent the Arctic. It uncovered some of the techniques of news storytelling, and reflected on the strengths and weaknesses of these sources of information. Section 4 explored the more imaginative journeys that artists, writers, musicians and others have undertaken with the Arctic as their theme. It presented a case for drawing on a wide range of representations of an environment – artistic as well as journalistic, geographic and scientific – in order to make sense of a place or a phenomenon. The last section reviewed five hundred years of exploration and exploitation of the Arctic, and introduced the concept of sovereignty as a means of understanding and managing conflicts of interest. It concluded by prompting some thoughts about the different ways in which people think about the Arctic environment, its habitats and inhabitants, and their own 'claim' to the region.

After completing Part 1 you should be able to:

- understand the nature and significance of maps as representations of environments and influences on attitudes towards environments
- recognise the nature and effects of the media in understanding environmental issues
- explore the relationship between the Arctic and artistic forms
- appreciate the significance of state sovereignty in the exploration, exploitation and development of the Arctic
- further develop skills of reading, communicating and accessing information.

Answers to SAQs

SAQ 1.1

1 The area between the North Pole and the northern treeline, which marks the northernmost places where trees will grow successfully. This area is also often expressed as the area where the average temperature for the warmest month (July) is below 10 °C.

2 The Arctic is far from 'empty' or uninhabited and the indigenous peoples of the Arctic are culturally diverse. The region's population of four million includes more than thirty different indigenous peoples and many languages.

3 Bathymetric maps showing the contours under the Arctic Ocean have taken on a more urgent political significance in the early years of the twenty-first century as some national governments (e.g. Russia, Canada and the US) prepare for disputes about sovereignty and access to mineral wealth in the region.

4 Animated maps can show the reductions in the area of summer sea ice in recent years quickly and simply. These mappings provide the basis of media stories about the issue.

SAQ 1.2

Journalists tend to emphasise the 'human interest' angles in any story and can therefore distract people from engaging with the underlying physical processes. They also consistently use similar images as a form of shorthand (for example polar bears). These images can create or underpin clichéd, limited and sometimes false representations of environmental change issues, and induce boredom. The limited space and time they have to produce their stories can mean that some of the attempts to condense complex issues leave the public with a dangerously simplistic notion of, in this case, the Arctic and processes of environmental change. Another problem derives from the journalistic practice of favouring conflict in stories. This can lead to an unbalanced presentation of the science of climate change. For example, the very small number of sceptics (who argue that human-induced climate change is probably not happening) have sometimes been given equal weight to the climate science community (who almost universally believe that it is).

SAQ 1.3

1 $32 \times 225 \times 0.2 = 1440$ kg or 1440 coffins' worth.

2 According to Table 3.2, replacing five bulbs would save 40 kg of CO_2 per year. So replacing ten bulbs would save 80 coffins' worth of CO_2.

SAQ 1.4

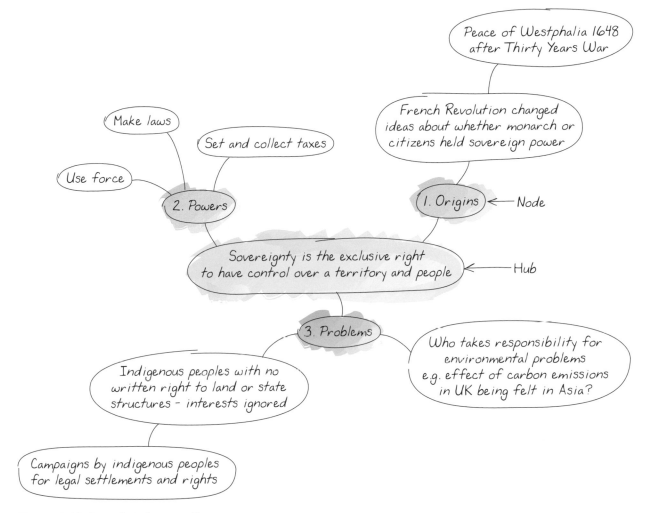

Figure 1.44 Completed spray diagram

SAQ 1.5

Bathymetric maps show the topography – the shape – of the Earth's surface under the sea, so they reveal continental geology. This is important because the Law of the Sea permits nation states to extend their national territory claims if they can demonstrate the extent of, for example, undersea ridges, and hence the extent of their sovereign interests. Climate change promises to make the large estimated reserves of minerals of the Arctic more accessible as higher temperatures melt sea ice, permafrost and land-based ice sheets. For this reason research into the form of the seabed relates to knowledge of climate change and debates about the UN Convention on the Law of the Sea.

References

America.gov (2007) 'U.S. Officials Cite Benefits of Joining Law of the Sea Convention', 13 June 2007, http://www.america.gov/st/washfile-english/2007/June/20070613113224eaifas0.4741785.html (Accessed September 2008).

Bird, K. J., Charpentier, R. R., Gautier, D. L., Houseknecht, D. W., Klett, T. R., Pitman, J. K., Moore, T. E., Schenk, C. J., Tennyson, M. E. and Wandrey, C. J. (2008) Circum-Arctic Resource Appraisal: Estimates of Undiscovered Oil and Gas North of the Arctic Circle, U.S. Geological Survey, Fact Sheet 2008–3049.

Clegg, P. (2005) *Three Made Places*, http://www.capefarewell.com/expeditions/2005/blog/day-9.html (Accessed May 2008).

Franklin, J. (1998) *Journey to the Polar Sea*, Köln, Konemann.

Hartley, A. (2005) 'Nymark (Undiscovered Island)', http://www.liverpoolmuseums.org.uk/conservation/exhibitions/capefarewell/alex_hartley.asp (Accessed September 2008).

McGhee, R. (2005) *The Last Imaginary Place: A human history of the Arctic world*, Oxford, Oxford University Press.

Pullman, P. (2007) http://www.guardian.co.uk/books/audio/2007/dec/20/books (Accessed September 2008).

Religion, Science and the Environment (2007) 'The Icefjord Commitment' 6 September 2007, http://www.rsesymposia.org/more.php?catid=173&pcatid=162 (Accessed January 2009).

Watt-Cloutier, S. (2005) 'Our land is changing – soon yours will too', *The Guardian*, 15 January.

Part 2
Time in context

Mark Brandon

Introduction

Part 1 of this block introduced ideas about how the Arctic is perceived through creative writing and artworks. Historical records and maps have also informed the view of the Arctic. In Parts 2 and 3 the block moves into looking at how science is changing the way we all view the Arctic. But first, what drives scientific enquiry and what are its particular characteristics?

Scientists observe, and ask questions about how the world works: for example, 'Is there a reason for the shapes of oceans and continents?', 'What is the nature and origin of stones on a beach?' and, particularly important in current environmental science, 'What does the observed evidence suggest might happen to this area/organism in the future?' Often such overarching questions can be answered only by narrowing down to a more precise question, for example 'How does the depth of the Atlantic Ocean vary between Europe and America?' These more precise questions can then be investigated experimentally; for example, we can measure the depths of the oceans by using sonar. Such investigations usually result in numerical measurements of the quantities or proportions of things – quantitative data. This data can then be used to create a simplified 'model' of the way that part of the world 'works'.

Scientists are usually cautious about the extent to which their research data produces unequivocal answers to such questions. Experimental data is usually subjected to statistical analysis to examine how reliable it is, and then the data is used to provide evidence – albeit sometimes overwhelming – rather than absolute proof that the world works in a particular way. So the often-used phrase 'research proves that…' is a misrepresentation of the process. The best that can be stated is 'research currently shows that…', because scientists are always checking and testing each other's work and looking for errors or inconsistencies. Scientific techniques such as measuring distances or analysing bubbles trapped in ice tend to change and improve over time, leading to more accurate data, and models of the ways the world works can lead to new and more searching ways of enquiring about our environment. One scientific enquiry may also lead to another – for example, a scientist who found the remains of a tree in the Arctic, or the presence of coal, would want to know how they got there. This process of continual questioning, testing and modelling, then asking further questions, has led to significant changes in how scientists and many others view the Arctic. It is no longer considered a remote and isolated place of little consequence.

The Arctic, like any region, has always undergone processes of change, which we can deduce from quite simple observations, but there is evidence, for example in the decreasing sea ice cover, that the changes are happening faster. The Arctic is often considered a victim of climate change – and it is certainly feeling its effects – but I hope to show that Sheila Watt-Cloutier was right when she described the Arctic as a planetary barometer. Her passionate description of how small streams are now turning into raging torrents as climate change begins to bite and the ice retreats is a compelling image. The changes going on right now are already affecting the societies and species living here, and the processes and flows that are affecting the Arctic will, and already are, changing the whole planet.

In Part 2, I will present the evidence that the icy Arctic landscape of Svalbard was once bathed in tropical heat. Over time, the geological and physical processes described here have changed its landscape into the present form shown in Figure 1.9. A major agent for change in the Arctic has actually been the ice for which it is now justifiably famous – and yet apparently it may soon be gone. But the great ice sheets of the north did not just appear overnight. The last section of this part demonstrates that they grew over a surprisingly long time.

I will start by taking you on a walk along an Arctic beach, and describing how a scientist could interpret what we see around us.

The cold coast: Svalbard

2

The beach picture in Figure 1.9 was taken only about 600 miles from the North Pole, on Svalbard, the Arctic archipelago that was such an inspiration to the author Phillip Pullman. It is an Arctic land by any physical definition and it looks a bleak and barren place. In fact, Svalbard means 'cold coast' in Norwegian. But cold, desolate and rugged does not mean worthless. Everything that was pointed out in Figure 1.9, such as the wide valleys, the tree trunks on the beach, and even the snow, can tell us a lot about its environmental story. This includes how it was formed and how it has changed throughout history – and by history I mean millions of years rather than just the relatively recent human history. The beach picture even shows that Svalbard, while seeming quite remote and isolated in some of the map projections in Part 1, is actually closely linked to the rest of our planet (but more of this in Part 3).

Walking on a beach is an exciting thing to do. Observations of objects and features in the environment allow us to develop explanations for how it got that way, touching many branches of environmental science and perhaps many environmental issues. For example, in Figure 1.9 a simple observation is that ice floats. At first thought, floating ice may not seem particularly significant – after all, ice floats in a glass of water. But what this observation means is that solid water is less dense than liquid water. It sounds simple, but usually it is the other way around: the liquid form of a substance is usually less dense than its solid form.

For example, if you melt some wax in a pan, the solid stays at the bottom until it has all melted, because the solid is more dense than the liquid. The scientific explanation for this is that the atoms are more tightly packed together in solid wax than in molten wax. For water it is the other way round – in ice the atoms are packed together more loosely than when it is liquid – so ice is less dense than water and it floats. So in winter, water in lakes, rivers and the sea freezes from the top down and not the bottom up, and when an Inuit makes a hole in a frozen lake to fish there is liquid water beneath the ice and the fish survive. Can you imagine what would happen to the fish in a lake if ice was denser than water? The physical properties of water are unusual; I cannot think of another common substance that behaves like that. But this small fact has been critical to the development of Arctic communities and, it is not going too far to say, all life on Earth.

Another simple observation in Figure 1.9 is that there are tree trunks on the beach. Our working definition of the Arctic is that it is the region north of the treeline, where no trees grow. Is the presence of tree remains on the beach not strange? Subsequent sections return to the trees and how they got to this beach, but first to the stones beneath our feet.

2.1 Stones on the beach

On most beaches there are things to look at on the ground; for example driftwood or even pebbles. Looking down at the pebbles on the Svalbard beach, I can see a jumble of rounded stones lying here and there, just like on many other shorelines. But every now and then one comes across something that looks a little different – perhaps a flattish stone with unusual imprints on it, or even something that looks like a bone or a tooth. When I pick them up, they are heavy and clearly made of stone. These are *fossils*, which we now know are the remains of long-dead life on Earth. The assembled bones of giant *dinosaurs* are an impressive sight, but before reaching a museum they go through a time-consuming and skilled assembly job, as they were most likely found as small fragments just like the ones you can see on some Svalbard beaches.

Figure 2.1 shows fossils of the shells of sea creatures that lived millions of years ago and were found on a Svalbard beach. On the left is a shellfish that lived on the sea floor and on the right a more mobile, swimming animal. When they died the swimmers sank to join the shellfish on the seabed. In the oceans, sediment is always falling to the seabed and can be made up of dust brought out to sea by the winds, dead sea creatures, tiny shells of plankton or even mud washed into the sea from the land. The rate at which sediment falls seems unbelievably slow – rates of 2 cm every 1000 years are not uncommon, and a clam shell 4 cm thick would take 2000 years to be buried. However, compared with the almost unimaginably long time period over which the Earth has existed, this burial is almost instantaneous. Over very long periods of time the sediment layers can turn into a relatively soft stone called a *sedimentary rock* (Figure 2.2), and if the type of sediment that falls changes over time, then the distinct layers are called *strata*. Through subtle chemical exchanges between the dead animals (or plants) and the sediment, very occasionally the remains can turn to stone along with the sediment around it, and so remain for us to find on a beach millions of years later. I use the term occasionally because not every animal

Figure 2.1 Two fossils of sea creatures collected on a beach in Svalbard

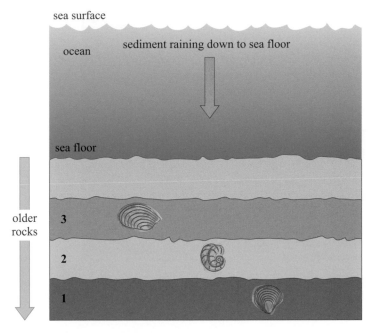

Figure 2.2 Schematic of the burying of fossils on the sea floor in a sedimentary rock. Fossils found in layer 1 are older than those in layer 2, and the youngest are in layer 3.

or plant that has ever lived has been turned into stone, only the tiniest fraction of them, but this is enough for scientists to learn about life that lived on the Earth before humans. The sorts of animal that are found in the fossil record change through the rock strata, reflecting the evolution of life. So if the species of shellfish that is present in the deepest (and oldest) rocks of level 1 in Figure 2.2 died out, shells exactly the same would not be found in levels 2 and 3 because the species no longer existed when those layers were formed.

Sedimentary rocks make very popular building materials – you may have heard of Portland Stone, named from Portland, Dorset, where it is quarried. This stone was used to build many British cities because it is very easy to cut along the strata and is a beautiful white colour. Did you realise, though, that if you look carefully at the Portland Stone in the buildings it is quite easy to spot fossil shells in them?

An obvious question to ask is that if the shells are buried at the sea floor, how is it that they are found when walking on the Svalbard beaches? The answer, whilst possibly fairly obvious to us now, was so disturbing that it took a very long time for the reasons to be both formulated and generally accepted.

When you walk along the Devon coast (Figure 2.3) you can easily see the strata in the cliffs that were formed through the process similar to that

Figure 2.3 Orcombe Rocks on the south coast of Devon. You can easily see layers that were formed as the rocks were laid down millions of years ago.

shown in Figure 2.2 (if you look closely you can even see them in the background of Figure 1.9). Early geologists could see the layers just as easily, but it took true genius to understand that the rocks were formed by the raining down of sediments, and are older at the bottom than they are at the top. This is the *Law of Superposition*, first formulated in the sixteenth century. What it means is that fossils embedded in the rock at the bottom of the cliff in Figure 2.3 are older than the fossils embedded in the top of the cliff. It sounds simple and obvious but it is only in the last century that scientists have been able to demonstrate that the Earth is approximately 4.5 billion years old and so is old enough to have formed the huge thicknesses of sedimentary rocks seen in places like Dorset and East Devon. If you walk along the bottom of the cliff where the strata are horizontal (as in Figure 2.3), any fossils embedded in the rock strata will all have died during a similar time period millions of years ago. However, it is more common to encounter sloping rock layers.

When the layers are at an angle to sea level, walking along a beach means crossing strata. As the animals and plants in successive strata change, the fossils embedded in the layers of rock change as well (Figure 2.4). Using the law of superposition, because the layers are sloping, a walk along the beach is actually a journey through time revealed by the fossils and the rocks. At different points along the beach different fossil animals and plants will appear and disappear as they evolve. A 20-minute walk in a region with sloping sedimentary strata can take you back in time (or forwards, depending on the direction you walk) past fossils of animals and plants that existed millions of years apart in the Earth's history.

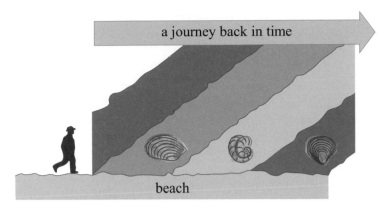

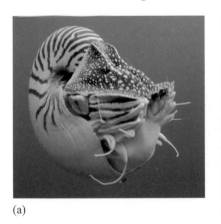

Figure 2.4 A schematic of a walk along a Svalbard beach. A walk along this beach is a journey in time through the layers that were laid down horizontally in Figure 2.2.

Let us come back to the question of *how do the fossils get on to the beach in the icy wastes of Svalbard?* And for that matter *how could sea creature fossils end up at the top of a cliff such as that in Figure 2.3?* One way to try to understand the fossils is to look for similar organisms living today. For example, the spiral fossil called an ammonite, shown in Figure 2.1, has a living descendant called the nautilus (Figure 2.5).

(a)   (b)

Figure 2.5 (a) A nautilus swimming in warm tropical waters; (b) the shell of a nautilus cut in half

The nautilus is a *cephalopod* and in the same biological family that includes squid and octopus – you can see the tentacles in the photograph. Figure 2.5(b) is a nautilus shell in cross-section and you can see that the structure is very similar to that of the fossil ammonite in Figure 2.1. The shell is very thin and fragile and it is easy to imagine that a fish or other predator that took a nautilus for food would smash the shell to get at the animal inside. This means that very few complete nautilus shells would ever reach the seabed in one piece and ones that do would not all be preserved as future fossils. Ammonites and their very similar descendants – the nautilus – have existed on the Earth for perhaps the last 500 million years. Throughout all of that time it is likely that they lived in similar environmental conditions in the world's oceans. But the surviving species shown in Figure 2.5 actually live within 30° latitude of the equator and close to coral reefs! How is it possible that the fossil of an animal whose descendants live near the equator in warm tropical seas is found on a beach and trapped in the rock strata on Svalbard – a group of islands very close to the North Pole with no warm equatorial waters and definitely with no living corals and nautilus?

Activity 2.1   The environment animals live in

Take a moment to think about the possible reasons why the fossils of the ancestors of animals such as the nautilus, which lives only in tropical marine seas, could be found in the polar regions.

Discussion

The most obvious answer is that the climate on Earth has changed over the last 500 million years. You read in Block 1 that the Earth was possibly warmer at the time the ammonites lived. Could it have been warm enough for Svalbard to be a tropical land surrounded by corals, much like the climate of northern Australia today? That is an enormous difference. Such a change in the climate of the Earth may be hard to conceive of, but the other possible explanation was even harder for scientists and the general public to accept: the Svalbard archipelago may once have been closer to the equator.

Summary of Section 2

Section 2 has discussed some of the basic geological features that are found on some Svalbard beaches. An observation of fossils on a beach or embedded in a cliff face shows that there are sedimentary rocks nearby. Sedimentary rocks are made from layers of sediment consisting of dust, mud and the shells of long-dead plankton laid down over millions of years. Over this time period compression of the layers (or strata) leads to the sediment being turned into a relatively soft rock. Sometimes trapped in the strata are the preserved bones and shells of long-extinct animals, which can be exposed as the sedimentary rock erodes. Looking at the species of the fossils can give an idea of the past climate. While the title 'cold coast' is appropriate today, given the evidence from the fossil record, the rocks that make up the island of Svalbard were once in a much more tropical climate. The presence of ammonites – an ancestor of the nautilus – demonstrates that there must once have been a tropical climate rather similar to that in northern Australia today.

The wandering continents

3

We now know that Svalbard and Greenland, and indeed all the continents, have not always been at the same latitudes and longitudes where they are today. It is an amazing idea, but perhaps even more surprising is that they still are moving today. Once the first semi-accurate maps of the globe were created, some people noticed what today seems quite obvious: the shapes of some of the continents today fit together strikingly well.

Figure 2.6 shows a pair of maps drawn in 1858 by the French geographer Antonio Snider-Pellegrini, demonstrating exactly this fact. Although a great scientist of his age, Snider-Pellegrini thought that the force needed to break up the continents in Figure 2.6 came from the Bible's Great Flood. Today there is much more evidence than 'they look like they fit together', but what Snider-Pellegrini and the person who developed the idea of **continental drift** – the German Alfred Wegener (Box 2.1) – first looked at were fossils. Wegener noticed that the distribution of particular species of fossils found today in different continents match up amazingly well. For example, fossils of the ancient fern *Glossopteris* are found in all of the major land masses of the southern hemisphere (Figure 2.7). While it is conceivable that plant seeds could be distributed around the Earth by ocean currents and winds, the same cannot be true for the reptile *Mesosaurus*. Fossils are found in both South America and Africa, but *Mesosaurus* could never have swum the 7000 km between them on today's Earth. This is a tiny part of

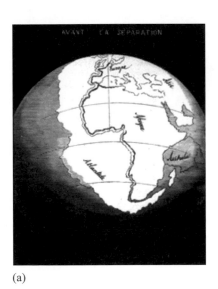
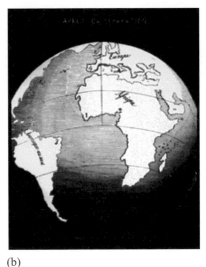

(a)   (b)

Figure 2.6 The continents of the southern hemisphere (a) before and (b) after separation, as drawn in 1858 by Antonio Snider-Pellegrini

the evidence that Wegener used to propose the then hugely controversial theory of continental drift. Perhaps the biggest reason why it was so difficult to accept was that, while Wegener proposed that land masses move around the planet to join and collide with each other, he could not imagine a physical force that could actually move continents. One reason for his failure was that, while the evidence was growing for the existence of a single supercontinent in the past, the oceans were virtually unstudied at this time. Perhaps they held the secret of the mysterious mechanism?

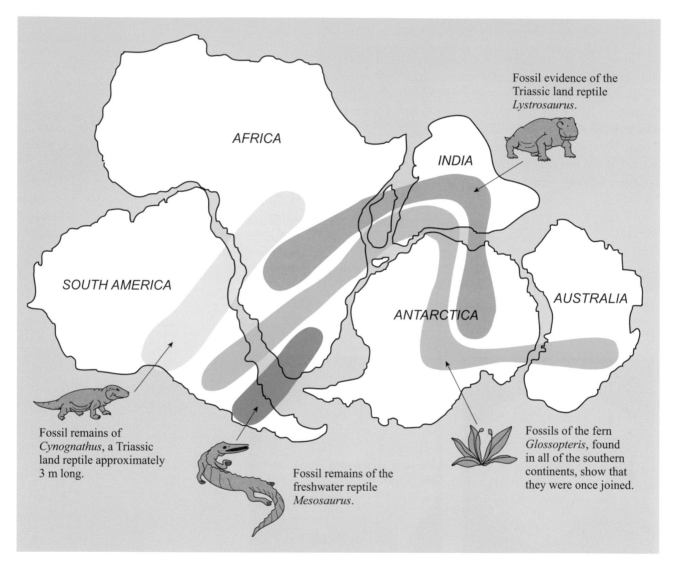

Figure 2.7 The distribution of similar fossils is just one of the pieces of evidence that demonstrates that in the past the continents were joined together

Box 2.1   Alfred Wegener (1880–1930)

Alfred Wegener (Figure 2.8) was born in Berlin and started his scientific career in 1904. He was a polymath with interests in many areas of science, but found his true calling when as a meteorologist he visited Greenland on a scientific expedition from 1906 to 1908. He pioneered the use of weather balloons to investigate air circulation, but he was also interested in the fossils he found. Back at the University of Marburg, Wegener noticed that, as in Figure 2.7, similar fossils can be found in widely spaced continents. This and other evidence, allied to the maps created by scientists like Snider-Pellegrini, led Wegener to propose in 1915 that all land was once connected in a giant supercontinent called Pangaea ('whole Earth' in ancient Greek – see Figure 2.6 and Table 2.3 in Block 1). If the continents were once part of a supercontinent, then the similarity of fossils would be easily explained; after all, the animals could just walk around. The argument was compelling, but because he could not produce a mechanism for the break-up of Pangaea (and his peers did not consider him a geologist), his idea of continental drift was not considered 'scientific'. Society can often be perceived as resisting changes for the better, and academia is no different. His outstanding contribution was ridiculed and never accepted in his lifetime. Wegener was not a bitter man and after a relatively short, successful career with contributions to many disciplines, he died in 1930 on a scientific expedition on the Greenland ice cap. It would take until the late twentieth century before his ideas were accepted and his contribution to geology internationally recognised.

Figure 2.8 Alfred Wegener on a scientific expedition in Greenland

Had he been alive when the next part of the story evolved he would surely have been at the forefront of developments. In a fitting tribute, the German polar research institute, the Alfred Wegener Institute, was named after him when it was founded in 1980.

Throughout human history boats have been used for travel, trade and, as Part 1 showed, exploration across the vast natural barriers of the oceans. It did not take ancient mariners long to realise that away from the navigational hazards of the rocky shallows close to shore, water depth rapidly increased and it was relatively safe. This meant that up until the nineteenth century there were hardly any measurements of how deep the seas actually were. It is not hard to see why, because until the late 1930s the only way to measure water depth was to use a line with a weight on the end and lower it to the sea floor! In deep waters a single depth measurement (sounding) could take several hours and a lot of effort. During the Second World War sonar (*SO*und *N*avigation *A*nd *R*anging) was developed for hunting submarines. Put simply, a ship would send out a pulse of sound ('ping'), which would be reflected by the submarine and it could then be detected back on board the ship. Scientists realised that the underwater pings could also detect the depth to the sea floor. If you measure the time it takes for a ping to be heard again, and you know the speed of sound in water, then you can work out the water depth very quickly.

Study note: using equations

The key to understanding equations is the interpretation of the equals sign. It is not just a convenient way of linking two expressions: it states that the two quantities lying on either side of it are exactly equivalent. If a change is made to one of the two expressions then that disturbs the equality. You can see this clearly from the equations that follow.

$$2 = 2$$

If you add a '1' to the left-hand side you can no longer legitimately use the equals sign:

$$2 + 1 \; does \; not \; equal \; 2$$

To retain equality a '1' must be added to each side:

$$2 + 1 = 2 + 1$$

This illustrates the basic rule of handling equations:

Whatever is done to one side of an equation must also be done to the other.

You can now apply this principle to changes that involve multiplication and division in expressions using symbols such as letters. All you need to do is move the letters around using the same rules that you would use for moving numbers from one side of an equals sign to another; the results will not be new letters, simply different arrangements of the original letters.

For example, with the starting equation

$$cost = price \times number$$

we can represent cost with the letter C, price with the letter P, and number with the letter N. So

$$C = P \times N$$

What steps must be taken to change this to an expression for number, N, in terms of cost, C, and price, P?

Dividing the right-hand side of the equation by P will give:

$\dfrac{\cancel{P} \times N}{\cancel{P}}$ which reduces to $1 \times N$, or just N.

To retain the equals sign you must carry out the same operation on each side of the equation, so the left-hand side must also be divided by P. Hence the expression becomes

$$\frac{C}{P} = N$$

As you do these sorts of manipulation, write down each step as you carry it out. This will enable you to make sure that you do precisely the same thing to each side. When you are experienced you will be able to move from the initial equation to the modified form in a single step.

Now you can do the same thing for an example involving distance, speed and time. You need to know that

$$\text{speed} = \frac{\text{distance}}{\text{time}}$$

Suppose you have been travelling at 100 km per hour for two hours. How far have you travelled? Can you write down what you did to get the answer as a series of mathematical expressions using the symbol v for speed, d for distance and t for time?

The equation (or formula) is

$$v = \frac{d}{t}$$

In order to calculate the vale of d, the equation is manipulated so that d is on its own on one side of the equation.

To retain equality the same operation must be carried out on both sides of the equation, so the full equation is

$v \times t = \dfrac{d \times \cancel{t}}{\cancel{t}}$ (t divided by t is 1)

So that leaves

$v \times t = d$

Putting the numbers in

$100 \times 2 = d$

Distance is 200 km.

SAQ 2.1   The depth of the oceans

A ship sends out a pulse of sound to the sea floor and the echo is heard 4 seconds later. If the speed of sound in seawater is 1500 metres per second, what is the depth of the water?

With sonar taking only a few seconds to record the depth of the ocean at any point, soon there was a rapidly expanding set of global measurements. Close to shore the seas are shallow, but on average the depth of the world's oceans is about 3730 m. What was most striking, though, was the discovery that there isn't a U-shaped valley between Europe, Africa and the Americas – as Figure 2.9 shows, the sea floor of the North Atlantic Ocean is shaped like a W.

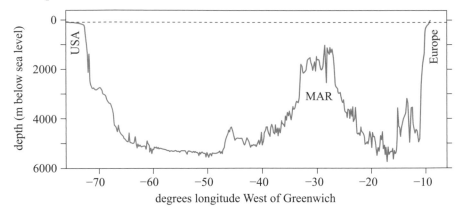

Figure 2.9 The depth of water along latitude 39° N. At the point –30° W is the Mid-Atlantic Ridge (MAR). Sea level is shown as a dashed line.

Between the continents of Europe and the Americas the central peak of the W is the largest mountain range on the planet – the 15 000 km long *Mid-Atlantic Ridge (MAR)*. The MAR is part of a larger 40 000 km chain that connects all of the world's oceans and it rises from the depths to actually break the surface at several locations such as Iceland, Bermuda and Ascension Island. What all these islands have in common is that they are *volcanically active*. A volcano is a crack in the Earth's crust that allows molten rock from deep underground to flow up to the surface. This molten rock is called *lava* and it rapidly cools to form crystals and a rock type called *igneous* rock. In many places the igneous rock extruded from a volcano can form the traditional volcanic cone that you may have seen in books or on holiday (Figure 2.10).

Figure 2.10 An active volcano on Iceland

Soon it was established that the huge mountain ranges beneath the surface of the oceans are volcanically active throughout their length. The American geologist and naval captain Harry Hess realised the implications: the volcanically active mountain ranges pour lava into the seas and this provides the force to push the continents apart. The idea of sea floor spreading was born, and the mechanism for continental drift that Wegener could only dream of had been found.

The familiar continental land masses above sea level sit on continuous units called *tectonic plates* (Figure 2.11). These plates are constantly in motion on the Earth's molten core.

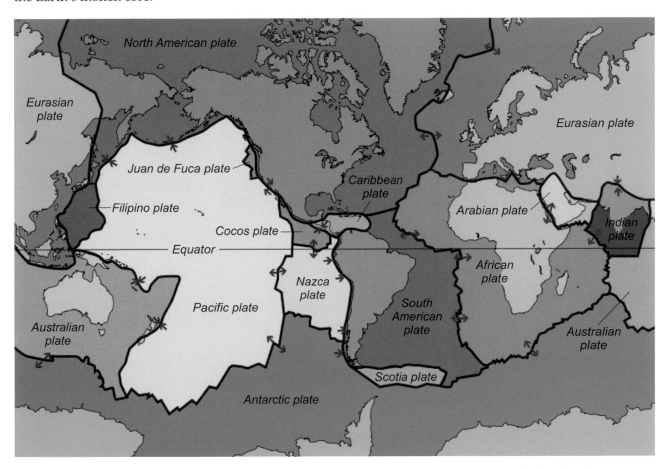

Figure 2.11 The current locations of the tectonic plates on Earth. The arrows show the relative directions of movement of the plates.

The arrows in Figure 2.11 show the relative directions of the movement of these tectonic plates. At a *constructive margin* like the MAR new sea floor is created and the plates are pushed apart, and every year the journey from England to the USA increases by about 2–4 cm. The fastest constructive margin discovered so far is the East Pacific Rise in the Pacific Ocean, where the plates are being forced apart at more than 10 cm per year.

With a mechanism to push the land masses apart it is obvious that they must also collide. When this happens there are several possibilities. When two oceanic plates collide, one descends beneath the other plate and this is called subduction at a ***destructive margin***. Subduction actually adds 'pull' to the 'push' provided at the constructive margin, and at these ***subduction zones*** are the deepest waters on Earth; for example, the Marianas Trench in the Pacific Ocean is more than 11 km deep. When plates collide on land, as one plate descends the other is pushed upwards, forming mountain ranges. Where the Indian and Eurasian plates are crashing into each other at a rate of about 9 cm per year (you can see this in the converging arrows in Figure 2.11) the Himalayan mountain range has been the result, and the highest mountain on Earth, Mount Everest (Chomolungma), is still rising at about 1 cm per year (Figure 2.12).

Figure 2.12 Mountain building as tectonic plates collide forms mountain ranges such as the Himalayas, the Andes and the Rockies. A clue to the relatively young age of the mountains here is the spiky and angular peaks, because erosion has not had time to make its mark.

Because rocks are pushed upwards as the plates collide, there is finally an answer to a question from Section 2 – how do fossils get to the top of a cliff? The strata in which the fossils were laid down have been lifted up as the tectonic plates collided, and as the plates buckled and shattered these same forces are responsible for tipping the strata in the way shown in the schematic of Figure 2.4. A simple schematic diagram of the processes that drive Wegener's continental drift is shown in Figure 2.13.

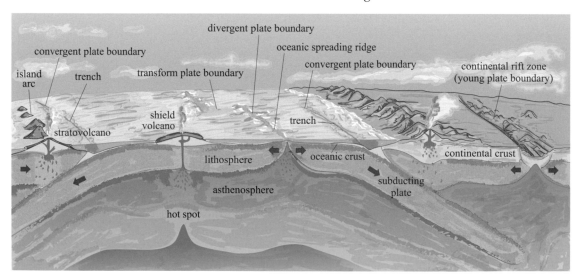

Figure 2.13 The processes that drive continental drift. In ocean basins, sea floor is created at constructive margins and destroyed in subduction zones. On land, mountain ranges are created as the plates collide.

While rocks are being created and destroyed by the slow dance of the tectonic plates, the movement of individual plates of perhaps a few centimetres per year may seem extremely slow (Figure 2.14), but think back to the four and a half-day walk of Block 1: this process has been going on for a very long time indeed.

Figure 2.14 Untold tragedies of Continental Drift, a cartoonist's view of the expanding oceans. Although slow to us, over hundreds of millions of years the forces have shaped our planet.

Because tectonic plates (Figure 2.11) expand and shrink at different rates, there is relative movement between them. A well-studied region, where sideways movement between two plates is important, is the Californian San Andreas Fault (Figure 2.15). Here the North American and Pacific plates are grinding against each other. This grinding is not a smooth process: sometimes the plates stick and the tension between them increases before they slip and the tension is reduced. As the plates slip there is an *earthquake* and anything in the vicinity of the slip will be moved. This moving can cause huge destruction and in 1906 – the last major movement in the San Andreas Fault – San Francisco was virtually destroyed and more than 3000 people were killed.

Figure 2.15 The North American and the Pacific tectonic plates meeting at the San Andreas Fault

Earthquakes are not rare events, because the plates are always moving. Usually they are relatively minor events, as the plates keep slipping, reducing the tension between them. Unfortunately, when they do stick and tension builds up, the large movements as they relax can result in huge loss of life when the tension is finally released. The 2004 Indian Ocean earthquake caused an ocean wave (tsunami) that killed almost a quarter of a million people, and the 2008 Chinese Sichuan earthquake killed almost 70 000 people. Because almost all earthquakes are along plate boundaries, a map of all of them in a 35-year period shows tectonic plate boundaries surprisingly well (Figure 2.16).

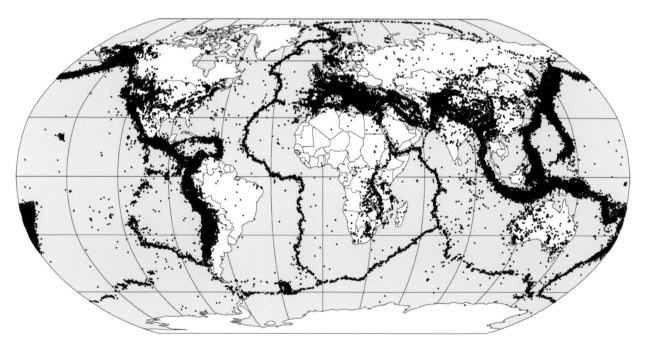

Figure 2.16 The locations of all earthquakes in the 35-year period from 1963 to 1998. They map the boundaries of the plates shown in Figure 2.11 very well.

Given the measurable rates at which the tectonic plates are moving, past reconstructions can be made – like that in Block 1 Figure 2.6 – and it is even possible to predict what the distribution of the continents is likely to be in the future. In just 100 million years' time Antarctica will have moved north and will have collided with Australia to create a new mountain range between them.

So back in deep time, Svalbard was closer to the equator and had a warmer climate. The Earth was warmer as well. These two factors meant that tropical sea creatures such as ammonites (Figure 2.1) could have survived. It also meant that fossil plants such as those shown in Figure 2.17 can now be found in large quantities. As mentioned in Part 1, such plant fossils provided one of the reasons for a rush to the north in the nineteenth century (Figure 1.33) because under certain special conditions, as plants die, over deep time they can turn into a substance that has become of paramount importance since the Industrial Revolution – coal.

Figure 2.17 Fossil leaves found on a beach in Svalbard

Summary of Section 3

Section 3 has discussed the evidence that led to the development of the theory of plate tectonics, starting with the simple observation that the continents seem to fit together and then moving on to the evidence from the fossil record. First proposed in the early twentieth century, it was generally accepted only once a mechanism for driving the movement of the tectonic plates had been established. This mechanism is from the combined forces from two processes: constructive plate margins that create new igneous rocks in volcanoes and which push the plates apart, and destructive plate margins such as ocean trenches that pull the plates. These processes move the tectonic plates across the Earth's molten core and have created the familiar distribution of continents of today. At the edge of the moving plates mountain ranges are created and there are very frequent earthquakes that are occasionally extremely destructive. These processes are still operating, and in the far future the distribution of continents on Earth will be very different.

4 Burning the past

In deep time 350 million years ago the Earth was in what is called the Carboniferous period (from Table 2.2 in Block 1 you can see that this is part of the Phanerozoic eon and the Palaeozoic era). The fossil record shows that Svalbard and its surroundings were hot, and the land was covered with swamps and forests. It was a world very different from our own, and our ancestors, the first mammals, would not appear for about another 100 million years. The only animals not in the oceans were insects and amphibians. If you think of what a tropical swamp looks like today, that is not very different from what Svalbard was like then, except with wildlife that would look very strange. Because the concentration of atmospheric oxygen was higher than it is now, insects could grow larger. For example, the Carboniferous dragonfly *Meganeura* had a wingspan of over 75 cm! Just as in any swamp, the plants grow and die in the water and mud. The scene I am describing is perfect for the formation of a substance that humans started to use for the first time on a large scale about two hundred years ago. That substance is *coal* – the fossil remains of long-dead plants and one of the fossil fuels mentioned in Block 1.

You probably recognise that when plants die they normally rot down, or decompose. In a swamp, they get buried in the muddy ground and without oxygen they decompose very slowly and produce methane (CH_4), some of which gets trapped in the peat. After about 10–15 000 years the carbon that was stored in the plants is concentrated so that it probably makes up about 50% of the total material and is known as peat. When peat is dried the carbon is concentrated enough to burn, and peat is still used as a fuel in some parts of the world. As it burns, of course, it gives off carbon dioxide (CO_2) and releases methane (CH_4), the two gases described in Block 1 as responsible for most of the enhanced greenhouse effect. Peat is a step on the way to coal – if you don't mind waiting a while. Actually, quite a long time. As more organic matter from the swamp and other sediment is rained down on top of the peat over millions of years, it builds up into a sedimentary layer just like those seen in Figure 2.3. As the layers are compressed, the temperature and pressure within them increase and the carbon is concentrated even more. Depending on how much the temperature and pressure increase, over time coal, natural gas or oil can be formed and collectively these are given the name *hydrocarbons*. The highest-quality coal, called anthracite, is a sedimentary rock that has been subjected to pressure and temperatures that cause it to change or metamorphose into a *metamorphic* rock. Almost 90% of anthracite is carbon and it burns at a very high temperature. In Svalbard the coal is called bituminous coal, and the carbon makes up 70–80% of the rock. It is an excellent fuel.

SAQ 2.2   Extracting energy from the rock

Burning coal extracts energy from the rock. Where did this energy originally come from?

The plants in the carboniferous swamp photosynthesised when they grew and trapped the carbon from carbon dioxide in the air into their fabric. When they died, because the plants did not decay the carbon was buried and stored deep underground. Burning coal burns plants that grew over 300 million years ago. Despite the irony of finding the deposits from a tropical forest on Svalbard, coal and the relative ease of finding it was – as shown in Part 1 – a key driver for the developed world to rush to this particular polar island.

Summary of Section 4

This section has pointed out the link between the movement of continents over deep time and the presence in Svalbard of our current largest source of energy: coal and other hydrocarbons. These resources were formed in tropical regions many hundreds of millions of years ago when the planet was warmer, and are the direct product of plant growth and then carbon storage as these plants died and were preserved. Using hydrocarbons utilises an energy source that originally came from the Sun. The burning of these fuels releases gases into the atmosphere that are responsible for the enhanced greenhouse effect.

5 The ice world

Among the fossils and coal on some Svalbard beaches is the occasional rock that is quite different from the others. Figure 2.18 shows an example. The randomly orientated blobs of orange, black and white are minerals that make up this igneous rock, which is called granite and is very similar to a type of rock that is very common in parts of the UK such as Cornwall.

Figure 2.18 A relatively unusual rock found on the beach in Svalbard. It has large, randomly orientated blobs of colour.

This rock is quite unlike the fossil-bearing sedimentary strata behind the beach that most of its pebbles and rocks come from. It does not appear to have a local origin. So just how did this igneous rock get here?

The evidence for the most likely means by which the granite arrived lies in the rounded hilltops all around, and in the background of Figure 1.9. The same irresistible force that rounded those hills most likely brought the stone in Figure 2.18 to the beach – that force was ice.

When Dante wrote *The Divine Comedy* in the fourteenth century he was showing the world his vision of hell. His idea was of nine circles of ever-increasing depth; the greater the sinner you were, the deeper the circle you were placed in, and so the greater eternal punishment you would suffer. For example, in the first circle were people who were not sinful as such, but they did not accept Christ. Here there were green fields, a castle and ancient Greek philosophers like Socrates and Plato to talk to. That doesn't sound too bad does it? However, by the sixth circle you would be down with the heretics in flaming tombs. Going ever deeper, the ninth and deepest circle was reserved for the very worst sinners. They would be punished for all time in the most awful conditions that Dante could think of.

Ignoring the actual sin, the punishment is probably not what you would expect. The most common cultural vision of hell is of fire and brimstone and people roasting. For Dante, fire and brimstone only made it to the sixth circle. He saved his most terrible punishment for the most serious sinners – they would be buried up to their necks in ice (Figure 2.19).

Figure 2.19 The artist Gustav Doré's etching of Dante's ninth circle of hell. The sinners are tortured in the horrors of the frozen lake of Cocytus.

Does that seem strange in these days of global warming, that his greatest punishment – and so I assume fear – was ice?

As a polar scientist I think Dante was on to something here. Being really cold is not like being chilled at a bus stop and moaning a bit: it is about experiencing truly awful pain, and cold can burn exposed flesh as badly as any heat. As well as the threat to human comfort at extremely low temperatures, turning water to ice can make it extremely destructive. Once the hills and mountains in the background of Figure 1.9 would have had peaks just like the relatively young ones in the Himalayas (Figure 2.12), but now they are rounded and smooth. Ice acting as nature's jackhammer and bulldozer provided the forces that eroded the peaks away.

As well as eroding mountains by grinding them down, the effect of ice can be more subtle but just as devastating. Many home owners will attest the fact that the expansion of water as it freezes can fracture pipes. In the hills and mountains, water seeps into small cracks in the rock. Successive freezing and expansion widens the cracks and shatters the rock to generate huge quantities of the sharp-edged rubble called *scree*. Scree can be seen on the flanks of many UK mountains and it is there on the hills in Figure 1.9. This scree rubble is then pushed and dumped into apparently random piles by the ice. Such sights can be seen all over Svalbard and they tell us that ice has played a key part in shaping the environment.

5.1 Snowfall

Oh the weather outside is frightful,

But the fire is so delightful,

And since we've no place to go,

Let It Snow! Let It Snow! Let It Snow!

(A popular Christmas song by Sammy Cahn and Jule Styne, 1945)

The British have always had a special place in their hearts for the weather. Britain has such a mild, temperate and friendly climate that it does not take much of anything to upset what is actually quite a fine balance. Too much rain and it floods, too much sun and everyone boils in a heatwave. But for real chaos in the UK what could be prettier – or more rapid in its impact – than just one little inch (2.54 cm) of snow? Figure 2.20 shows the media's view of the impact. It is fair to note that people in many parts of the world would laugh at the thought of 2.5 cm of snow crippling Britain (Figure 2.21), but apparently it did. For the UK, snow generally comes quickly and causes chaos because people are just not used to it. Apart from the odd unusually harsh winter such as in 1947 and 1962–63, snow is usually gone just as quickly as it arrives. It is a short-term and transient thing; the phrase 'cold snap' is common.

But what happens to the snow when the air temperatures are low enough to stop it melting away in summer?

One inch of snow causes chaos - and there's five more on the way

Last updated at 17:35 24 January 2007

💬 Comments (50) | ↘ Add to My Stories

Transport bosses were slammed today over the travel chaos caused by an inch of snow, while commuters are bracing themselves for even worse delays tonight after forecasters claimed there could be five inches more snow between 4pm and 7pm.

The Met Office has issued a number of severe weather warnings today for the whole of the South-East and said there could be further snow throughout the day.

A commuter scrapes snow from his car on his way into work this morning.

Figure 2.20 The newspaper *The Daily Mail* had a particularly British view on the benefits of snow to the UK!

When snow first settles it is usually light and fluffy because there is a lot of air trapped between the individual flakes. As more falls and it builds up in thickness the older snow underneath is squeezed and the air-filled gaps between the flakes are reduced in size. Eventually the gaps between the flakes become smaller and smaller and they are soon completely closed off from contact with the atmosphere. At this point the snow has turned to solid ice containing isolated trapped bubbles of air. Because the process of snow changing to ice depends on the weight of the snowfall, it usually takes quite a lot of snow to create ice at the bottom. In the middle of that famously cold continent of Antarctica you would have to dig quite a way to reach ice.

For example, at the South Pole you would first dig through light, fluffy snow. Then it would become harder and harder to dig as the amount of air trapped in the snow reduced. This would continue getting ever more difficult until eventually, at about 115 m depth, the air bubbles would become isolated and the snow would have completely turned to ice. One hundred and fifteen metres of snow, a huge amount, and certainly much more than I would ever want to dig.

In Svalbard, which has a wet maritime climate, the snow is much denser than in Antarctica and it can take only a few metres of snowfall before you reach ice.

Once a large amount of ice has formed beneath the snow cover it becomes a *glacier*. Once formed, of course, a glacier does not stay still. Because ice is close to its melting point it is relatively flexible. The American scientist Richard Alley memorably describes ice as a hot solid – one that is close to its melting point.

> In a freezer, an iron horseshoe and a chocolate bar are both stiff and brittle and neither will flow. In your back pocket, though, the horseshoe will remain stiff and brittle, but the chocolate bar will 'smoosh' as it warms near its melting point. Have a blacksmith heat the horseshoe white-hot, almost to melting and the horseshoe will become nearly as soft as the pocketed chocolate bar.
>
> *(Alley, 2000)*

So that is the key. Gravity acts on the ice and because the ice is close to its melting point it starts to flow downhill, just like liquid water would.

If a glacier is formed on a mountain then it will flow down a valley. You may have heard the phrase 'river of ice' (Figure 2.22); the flow in a glacier is of course much slower than any river you are used to (after all, just look in any dictionary for a definition of the word glacial) but it is in many ways similar. Although glaciers move slowly compared with us, their impact on the environment has been huge.

I am sure you will have heard that virtually all the glaciers on Earth are melting, but a small number are still advancing. These advancing glaciers can move tens or even hundreds of metres a year, pushing everything movable in the way – and they erode the things that are not movable.

Figure 2.21 Warning: skidoo traffic! In many parts of the world, including Svalbard, snow is just part of normal life.

Although that may seem slow, you are probably thinking again on a human timescale. Time can take on a different level of importance depending on how you perceive it. For example, what may seem quick to us would be very slow to a hummingbird, and during its entire life a glacier could appear stationary. In contrast, while I can quite literally run rings around a giant tortoise on a beach in the Galapagos Islands, it could be the same animal that Charles Darwin met when the *Beagle* visited the islands in 1835.

Figure 2.22 One of nature's bulldozers, the Daugaard–Jensen Gletscher in Greenland

As glaciers advance they push loose rubble and sediment in their way. This sediment, which consists of very large boulders as well as small fragments, gets entrained in the ice, turning into a something similar to a giant abrasive file. As the ice advances it grinds down the rocks beneath to leave scours and gouges in the bedrock that are aligned with the direction of ice flow (Figure 2.23(a)). You can see these scratch marks in many places around the world. On a larger scale, the once angular valleys of young mountain ranges become rounded and eroded into a wide U shape (Figure 2.23(b)). Rubble, including scree, is also pushed in front of and to the sides of glaciers – exactly like a bulldozer. This debris is called *moraine*.

You may like to take a look at some time-lapse videos of glacial motion. There are links on the course website.

Whilst observations of glacier motion can be made using scientific instruments and time-lapse photography, humans do not live long enough to see the larger-scale effects of the ice in action. However, the signature left by the ice is all around in the landscape. The rounded hills in the

(a)

(b)

Figure 2.23 The evidence of past glaciers: (a) glacial scouring on the bedrock; (b) an example of a U-shaped valley formed by glacial erosion

background of Figure 1.9 have been eroded away by ice that was on top of them. They have been formed by the same forces that produced similar U-shaped valleys all across the UK and tell us that Britain was also once ice-covered. You may not agree with Dante's vision of the horror of ice and the cold, but over the timescales of deep time, ice literally is a leveller. It grinds down and reshapes everything in its path. It may even be fair to suggest that after continental drift, ice more than anything else has shaped our planet.

5.2 Bubbles in the ice

In the previous section I talked about how air is trapped as the snowfall is turned to ice, and that in Antarctica it can take about 115 m of snow depth before reaching solid ice. The other great ice sheet on our planet is in the Arctic and covers Greenland; here one would have to dig perhaps 75 m through the snow to reach ice where the bubbles of air were completely closed off to the atmosphere (Figure 2.24). How many years of snowfall in the centre of Greenland would it take to reach a thickness of 75 m?

Snow is another form of precipitation, just like rain, except of course that the air temperatures are below 0 °C. The amount of rainfall is measured with a standard measuring jug, and to measure snowfall similar basic equipment is used – just a normal ruler. By measuring the snowfall (called the accumulation rate) at several places over the Greenland ice cap it is possible to produce a precipitation map for the whole country (Figure 2.25). Places on the map shown in Figure 2.25 with the same snowfall are joined together by lines called contours. Similarly contour shading joins together places of the same ice height.

Figure 2.24 Bubbles trapped in a piece of glacial ice found on an Arctic beach

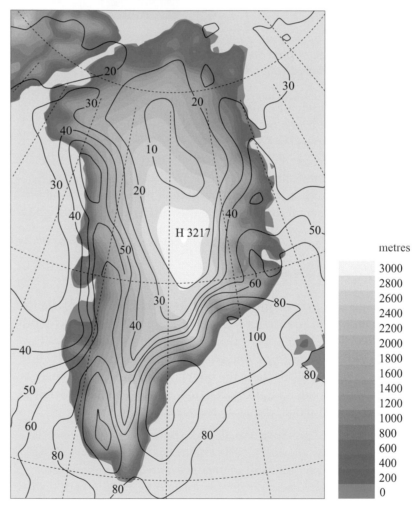

Figure 2.25 A map of Greenland showing average annual snowfall in centimetres per year using contours, and height of ice in metres above sea level using shading. Contour intervals for snowfall are 10 cm in the range 0–60 cm, and every 20 cm above that. Shading intervals for the ice height are every 200 m. The highest point of the ice in metres is marked as H 3217, which is 3217 m above sea level.

Activity 2.2   Annual snowfall on the summit of Greenland

Using the data shown in Figure 2.25, what is the annual snowfall at the highest point in Greenland?

Discussion

The highest point in Greenland, 3217 m, lies within the 3000 m contour. This is between the 20 cm and 10 cm annual accumulation rate contours, but it is difficult to estimate accurately. An estimate of 15 cm per year is not unreasonable, because the highest point is about halfway between the 20 cm and 10 cm snowfall contours.

An average of the actual annual snowfall reaching the summit of Greenland over a 600-year period is actually 24.6 cm per year. Looking at the newspaper headline in Figure 2.20 it is striking how small the snowfall in the centre of Greenland actually is. Less than ten times the amount that it takes to apparently bring the UK to a standstill. The reason it is so low is because when air is very cold it cannot hold much moisture, and it is the moisture which forms the snow. Around the edges of Greenland, where the air is wetter, particularly in the south-east corner, you can see that precipitation is much greater, at more than 1.2 m per year.

SAQ 2.3   How much snow has fallen?

On the Greenland ice sheet there is a layer of 75 m of snow before there is ice. If the annual rate of snowfall on the Greenland summit is 25 cm per year, how many years would it take for 75 m of snow to fall?

Hint: the first stage of your calculation should be to convert the annual snowfall per year into metres.

It could take almost 300 years for 75 m of snow to fall on the summit of Greenland, and so for the small bubbles to be completely closed off from the atmosphere. In reality our simple calculation does not tell the whole story because as the snow builds up it is compressed, and so turns to ice a little more quickly. The fact remains that it takes a much longer period than a human lifetime for the air pores in the snow to be closed off and ice to be created here. You will see the importance of this in Part 3. The thickness of the ice at the summit of Greenland is over 3000 m, so it must have taken a long time for the vast Greenland ice cap to develop. This could become an important factor in the future when considering how rapidly the ice cap could disappear with anthropogenic-induced climate change.

Summary of Section 5

This section has discussed the effects of snow and ice on the landscape seen today. The cold can be extremely destructive to rocks, first through the expansion of water in cracks as it freezes, through to larger-scale processes. Starting with a snow cover that survives the entire summer before being added to in successive winters, glaciers are formed. As a 'hot solid' the glaciers flow, pushing and entraining rubble in their fabric. This grinds down everything in an advancing glacier's path. Once-angular valleys were rounded into wide U shapes that can be seen over much of the Arctic as well as the UK, and there are deep scratches on the rocks that remain. The falling snow that originally formed the glaciers also traps air between the crystals, and as ice is formed the air remains trapped. This fact will become important in Part 3 of this Block.

Summary of Part 2

In this part I have discussed evidence from rocks and fossils that litter the beaches of Svalbard, the existence of coal in particular, that some Arctic regions were once not just slightly warmer than today, but that this island had a tropical climate. The main reason for this is continental drift over deep time, which has moved the region from the much hotter equator to the high latitudes where it is today. The other reason is past climate change, which will be investigated more in Part 3 of this block. Plate tectonics can create mountain ranges, but given time, erosion by ice leaves the rounded hills and smooth, wide valleys of the Arctic and much of the UK today. Finally, you have seen that the rate of snowfall on the summit of the Greenland ice sheet is a rather slow process and in human timescales it takes a surprising length of time for snowfall to reach a thickness that can close off the trapped air to the atmosphere. Part 3 will introduce more about the Arctic environment and some consequences of this interesting mix of timescales on the environment, and what it tells us about the Earth and its near future.

After completing Part 2 you should be able to:

- distinguish between sedimentary, igneous and metamorphic rocks and how they relate to each other
- describe the theory of continental drift, the processes that drive it and how Arctic lands were once closer to the equator
- understand and summarise the destructive power of ice on the landscapes we see today and the vast timescales that it has taken to form the current Arctic landscapes
- use simple equations to calculate unknown values.

Answers to SAQs

SAQ 2.1

Because the sound has travelled from the ship to the sea floor, and then back to the ship, it has actually travelled twice the depth of the water. To work out the time it takes to reach the sea floor, divide the time it takes to reach the ship by 2.

$$\text{time for sound to reach sea floor} = \frac{4}{2} = 2 \text{ seconds}$$

Multiply the time taken for the sound to reach the sea floor (t) by the speed at which the sound travels (v):

$$\text{depth of water } (d) = 2 \text{ seconds} \times 1500 \text{ metres per second}$$
$$\text{depth of water} = 3000 \text{ metres} = 3 \text{ km (as there are 1000 m in 1 km)}$$

So the depth of the water is 3 km.

SAQ 2.2

If you think back to Block 1, virtually all the energy reaching the planet's surface is from the Sun. Some of this energy has been converted to coal through photosynthesis in plants and then has been stored in the rocks. So burning fossil fuels is actually utilising energy from the Sun.

SAQ 2.3

The thickness of snow should be divided by the amount that falls each year to get the answer. First, though, convert the annual snowfall from centimetres per year to metres per year. There are 100 centimetres in a metre, so divide by 100.

$$\text{annual rate of snowfall} = \frac{25 \text{ cm per year}}{100}$$

so
$$\text{annual rate of snowfall} = 0.25 \text{ m per year}$$

and

$$\text{time for 75 m of snow to fall} = \frac{75 \text{ m}}{\text{annual rate of snowfall in m per year}}$$

$$\text{time for 75 m of snow to fall} = \frac{75 \text{ m}}{0.25 \text{ m per year}}$$

$$\text{time for 75 m of snow to fall} = 300 \text{ years.}$$

References and Further reading

Alley, R. B. (2000) *The Two Mile Time Machine*, Princeton, Princeton University Press.

Coley, D. A. (2008) *Energy and Climate Change*, Chichester, Wiley.

Fortey, R. (1997) *Life: An Unauthorised Biography*, London, HarperCollins.

Kunzig, R. (2000) *Mapping the Deep: The Extraordinary Story of Ocean Science*, London, W. W. Norton.

Macdougall, D. (2006) *Frozen Earth: The Once and Future Story of Ice Ages*, Berkeley, University of California Press.

Part 3
Following the flows

Mark Brandon

Introduction

1

Part 2 discussed the Arctic in the context of deep time from the perspective of a scientist making and interpreting observations about the fossils and extensive coal deposits present today in Svalbard. The scientific theory of plate tectonics suggests that at least some of these Arctic lands were once tropical. Since then the continents have moved and ice has changed the landscape. This part will concentrate on evidence from the last 800 000 years using information collected from ice cores from Greenland and Antarctica and will use this evidence to discuss current and possible future climate. The cores show that there have been nine periods in the recent past when large areas of the Earth were covered by ice. During the last 10 000 years – called the Holocene – there has been an unusually stable climate compared with the rest of the record, and the Holocene encompasses the entire development of human civilisation.

The Arctic, like any region, has always undergone climate change but there is evidence, for example in the decreasing sea ice cover, which suggests that the changes are happening faster. I intend to show how evidence from the ice cores suggests that flows of chemicals and energy dominate natural systems and cause these changes. I will discuss flows of water, heat and even pollution around the planet and show how, through positive feedback processes, the flows that are affecting the Arctic are already changing the whole planet. There will be further changes, with an impact on us all. The Arctic is often considered a victim of climate change – and it certainly is – but I hope to show that Sheila Watt–Cloutier was also right when she described the Arctic as a planetary barometer.

To discover the evidence that the Earth is dominated by flows I will start with that most famous Arctic animal of all – the polar bear.

2

A climate change icon

Part 1 pointed out that the polar bear has become an international climate change icon. But how much is known about this bear, its habitat and life? Part 4 of this block will talk about the role of language, but by way of introduction how about the name of this bear? To me it is the polar bear; to a German it is an *Eisbär* (ice bear) and to a French person it is an *ours blanc* (white bear). In these three examples the bear is referred to as polar, white, or an ice bear – eminently sensible. The Latin name for this bear is *Ursus maritimus*, made up of *Ursus*, which is bear, and *maritimus*, which means 'of the sea'. To us it is polar bear, but the Latin name says sea bear. The reason for this is given by the writer Barry Lopez:

> The polar bear is a creature of arctic edges: he hunts the ice margins, the surface of the water, and the continental shore. … He dives to the ocean floor for mussels and kelp, and soundlessly breaks the water's glassy surface on his return to study a sleeping seal. Twenty miles from shore he treads water amid schooling fish. In winter, while the grizzly hibernates, the polar bear is out on the sea ice, hunting. In summer his tracks turn up a hundred miles inland, where he has feasted on crowberries and blueberries.
>
> *(Lopez, 1986)*

Figure 3.1 shows the movements of one satellite-tracked female between 1994 and 1998 (Wiig, 2003). Over four years this bear travelled more than 14 500 km, covering an area of almost 500 000 square kilometres in search of its main prey species – the seal. The state of the seas and ice of the region will therefore directly affect the bears, but it turns out that there are also effects from much further afield.

Attaching a satellite tracking device to polar bears is not easy and they have to be drugged. This gives an opportunity for them to be weighed, measured, tagged, and have various samples such as hair, fat and teeth removed for later chemical analysis. The amount of body fat on a bear indicates whether it has been eating well or is starving. But a chemical analysis of this body fat gave a surprise: polar bears have measurable amounts of a family of chemicals called ***polybrominated diphenyl ethers (PBDEs)*** in their fat (Figure 3.2). The same discovery was made in Arctic ringed seals. PBDEs are a group of synthetic chemicals developed over the twentieth century as fire retardants. Fabrics and furniture are impregnated with them with the sole aim of slowing the rate at which they burn, and they have been very successful. However, once created, PBDEs are very difficult to destroy and will not break down into their elements over time. For this reason they are considered a ***persistent organic pollutant (POP)*** (Box 3.1).

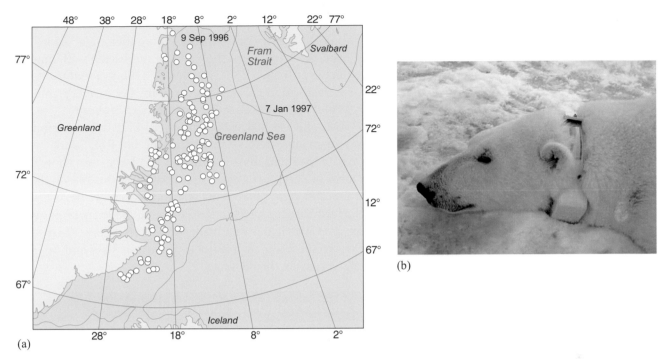

(a)

(b)

Figure 3.1 (a) **The travels of a female polar bear tracked over 1415 days between 1994 and 1998; also shown are the minimum (9 September 1996) and maximum (7 January 1997) ice extent** *(Source: adapted from Wiig et al., 2003)* **(b) A drugged polar bear with a satellite collar attached to its neck. Although it looks a tight fit the collar is carefully designed to expand as the bear grows, whilst not falling off as it moves about** *(Source: http://alaska. usgs.gov/science/biology/polar_bears/distribution.html, accessed November 2008)*

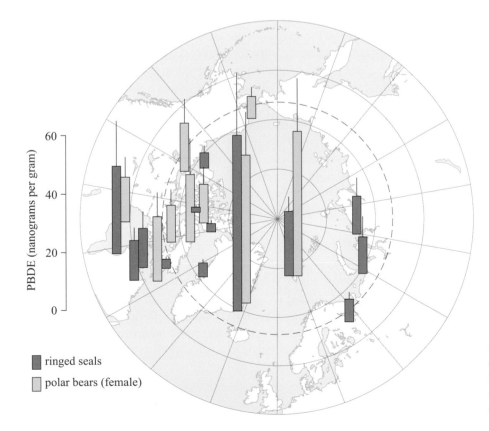

PBDE (nanograms per gram)

◼ ringed seals
☐ polar bears (female)

Figure 3.2 **The concentration of PBDE in the fat of polar bears and the ringed seal (one of their main prey species) at different sites across the Arctic**

In the early 1980s scientists began to detect POPs in the tissues of fish and shellfish close to populated areas. Concentrations were then detected in human breast milk, and the levels were shown to be increasing with time – perhaps through direct exposure to PBDEs or through *bioaccumulation*. The scale in Figure 3.2 is given in nanograms per gram. So, in every gram of the sample of bear and seal fat in East Greenland there is about 50 nanograms of PBDE. This is 0.000000005 grams of PBDE in every gram of sample. This may seem an extremely small amount, but PBDEs are potentially very toxic to liver and thyroid function and have been shown to hinder development of nervous tissue in mammals. For this reason the European Union banned several of them in 2004 and then more in 2008. The migration of PBDEs into humans and shellfish was explained by proximity to where they were used. While it is relatively simple to see how PBDEs can get into subjects close to their source, it is not so clear how they end up in polar bears and ringed seals in the Arctic.

Box 3.1   Pollution and bioaccumulation

The term 'pollutant' came up several times in Block 1, and it is a very wide-ranging term. When the introduction or action of something into our environment causes harm it is considered a pollutant. This could be a harmful chemical such as smoke from a chimney, or it could be a more subtle and transient effect such as floodlights at an evening football match preventing stargazing. There are many examples of how society has responded to pollution, such as the removal of lead in petrol which affected human health, or the banning of chlorofluorocarbons (CFCs), which damaged the ozone layer. In both these cases, when the pollution source was removed the levels of them in the environment reduced and consequently so have the effects – albeit with a time delay. By definition, persistent pollutants (POPs) such as PBDEs do not break down, so continued introduction of even minute levels of them into an environment leads to accumulation and perhaps magnification of potential harm. For example, at a landfill site the PBDE level is likely to increase with time. Animals around that landfill may ingest PBDEs directly, but the level that accumulates in their tissues may be so small that it does not cause problems to any particular animal. However, a predator such as a cat might eat dozens of rats that live around the landfill, so it would receive the combined dose that each of these rats had within it. If this dose were subsequently absorbed by the cat then the resulting accumulated level could be significantly more harmful. This concentration of pollutants at higher levels in the food chain is called **bioaccumulation,** and the result is that higher predators can be poisoned and suffer harm while animals at lower levels in the food chain are apparently unaffected.

Summary of Section 2

In examining the European name of the polar bear there is an apparent contradiction between its common and scientific names. This is because the polar bear is at home in the natural environments of land, sea and ice. In their search for food, bears can travel huge distances. Chemical analysis of the fat in the bears and their main prey species, the ringed seal, shows that they contain PBDEs – manufactured persistent organic pollutants that do not occur naturally.

3 The atmospheric and ocean flows

We now know that PBDEs end up in the Arctic through their physical transport by the winds, the ocean and the rivers of the world. All three mechanisms are important, but the most rapid carrier is the wind. The basic principle of global atmospheric circulation is simple: warm air rises and cold air sinks. The warming effect of the Sun is much greater at the equator than at higher latitudes and so the air is much warmer and it rises. At high latitudes the air cools and it sinks. This drives a horizontal wind. To help picture this, imagine a room with a radiator on one wall, and at the other end of the room an open fridge (Figure 3.3).

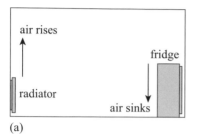

Figure 3.3 (a) A room with a radiator on one wall and an open fridge on the other will cause air to rise and sink at opposite ends; (b) horizontal winds are set up to replace this ascending and descending air

The radiator heats up the air around it, and the air rises in what is called a **convection current** all the way the to the ceiling and starts to spread. At the other end the fridge is doing the opposite and cooling the air, which sinks and spreads across the floor. To replace the air that has risen, the air beneath the radiator is pulled upwards and then heated and rises while the opposite is happening at the other end of the room.

At the most basic level, on Earth the same process is happening, with warm air rising from lower latitudes and sinking at higher, colder latitudes, so high-level winds tend to blow from the hotter regions to the colder. This general pattern is modified by the rotation of the Earth, which deflects the wind flow away from the apparently direct path.

These wind flows are further complicated by the distribution of continents across the globe and their mountain ranges. Winds are modified as they move around and over mountain ranges. They are also affected as they travel over land and sea surfaces where the air is warmed to different extents. This is because of two additional processes that affect the heating and cooling of the air. Land and sea surfaces reflect different amounts of solar energy falling on them and materials such as rocks and water need different amounts of heat to warm them up.

When solar energy reaches the Earth's surface a proportion of it is reflected straight back out into space and only the fraction which is not reflected heats the terrain. Different materials have a different **albedo** and so reflect a different amount of solar energy. If you put your hand on a black car on a warm sunny day, and then on a white car, you will notice that the black car feels warmer. This is because it reflects less energy so it heats up more. The black car has a lower albedo than the white car. Table 3.1 shows the albedo of some typical surfaces. For example, the surface of the ocean has an albedo of 3%, which means that 100% − 3% = 97% or almost all of the incoming energy from the sun actually heats the water. Fresh snow, on the other hand, reflects away most solar energy, a property that has important consequences for the climate of the Arctic.

Table 3.1 The albedo of typical features on Earth

Surface	Albedo
ocean surface	3%
conifer forest in summer	9%
grassy fields	25%
sea ice	40%
desert sand	40%
fresh snow	80–90%

SAQ 3.1   The importance of albedo

If the same amount of energy reaches a desert and sea ice on a frozen sea, what proportion of the energy is available to heat up the material? If snow then falls to cover the sea ice, what will be the amount of energy available to heat up the ice?

When energy reaches the surface of an object the amount the object heats up is determined by its *specific heat capacity*. This is a measure of how much energy it takes to raise the temperature of 1 kg of a particular substance by 1 °C. A lower specific heat capacity means that it takes less energy to heat up something, and vice versa. Although the term may be unfamiliar, the concept most likely is not.

Activity 3.1   The effect of specific heat capacity

On a very hot sunny day on a table outside in the sun there is a glass containing 1 kg of water (i.e. 1 litre), a 1 kg piece of cork and a 1 kg piece of iron. Ignore albedo effects and assume that all three items absorb the same amount of energy from the sun. How hot will each become after 1 hour? (Ignore all sources of heat except that directly received from the Sun.)

Discussion

You probably recognised that the 1 kg of iron would be the hottest. It does not take very much heat energy to change the temperature of the iron because it has a low specific heat capacity. The other two items are harder to place, but the cork will be cooler than the iron and finally the water, which has the highest specific heat capacity, will be the coolest item on the table.

Water has an extremely high specific heat capacity and it takes a vast amount of energy to heat it. This is why virtually all car engines use water in their cooling systems. Taking into account the combined effects of the albedo and specific heat capacity, even two adjacent areas, such as a beach and the sea lapping on it, will heat up by different amounts on a sunny day.

Areas with lower heat capacities and lower albedo heat up more. This heat is transferred to the air above so in these areas it will rise at a faster rate, and in cooler areas the air sinks. The rising and sinking air drives horizontal winds much as in Figure 3.3, although on a planetary scale.

Sea ice cover is also constantly moving. It is pushed by the winds and ocean currents and drifts in the pattern shown in Figure 3.4. The Svalbard beach picture had tree trunks on it (Part 1 Figure 1.9) and yet the Arctic was defined as being north of the treeline. How do the tree trunks get there? They are mostly Siberian fir trees (*Abies sibirica*), a native of the great forests of northern Russia. Tree trunks are carried out to sea in summer by rivers such as the Lena, the Ob, the Yenisei and Volga. Then they are frozen into the sea ice and travel in two ocean currents called the *Transpolar Drift Stream* and the *Beaufort Gyre*. Eventually they reach the shores of Svalbard and Greenland. Dating of these tree trunks using *carbon dating* shows that some are several thousand years old.

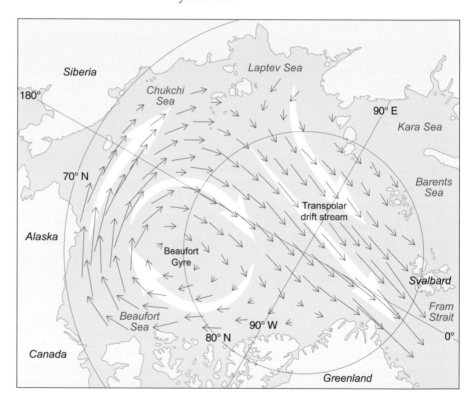

Figure 3.4 The mean ice drift across the Arctic Ocean. The ice is trapped in two major circulation features, the Beaufort Gyre and the Transpolar Drift Stream. White arrows show the general movement of the ocean currents; blue arrows show the general drift of the sea ice.

Box 3.2   Nansen and the voyage of the *Fram*

Wood on the shores of Svalbard and East Greenland caused confusion to the first explorers. But when wreckage from a ship called the *Jeanette* was found on the coast of East Greenland, the best environmental scientist of the age, the Norwegian Fridtjof Nansen (Figure 3.5), had a eureka moment. Nansen knew that the *Jeanette* had sunk off Alaska on the other side of the Arctic Ocean and deduced that the wreckage must have been carried across the frozen sea by the sea ice. He decided to try to use the ice drift to reach the North Pole and study the Arctic environment on the journey. He had the ship *Fram* (Norwegian for 'forward') built (Figure 3.5). The ship had a round hull so that it would not get crushed like the *Jeanette*, and he left Norway in 1893 for the Arctic and the North Pole. It was over three years before he and his colleagues returned.

(a)

(b)

Figure 3.5 (a) Fridtjof Nansen; (b) his ship the *Fram* frozen into the Arctic Ocean and drifting in the Transpolar Drift Stream

They followed the Russian coast and the *Fram* froze into the sea ice off Siberia. As they drifted northwards Nansen realised that the *Fram* was going to miss the pole so he and Hjalmar Johansen left the ship to make for the pole on foot. This was incredible. They knew the ship was drifting and they must have been certain that they would never find her again. The *Fram* survived the Arctic drift and reached Svalbard in the summer of 1896. Nansen and Johansen turned back just north of 86° N, having reached the highest latitude then attained. After an epic journey across the sea ice they endured the winter of 1895 on the island of Franz Josef Land (Zemlya Frantsa Iosifa) and then caught a ship back to Norway. After the long separation they arrived three days before the *Fram* in August 1896 (Figure 3.6).

After the expedition Nansen became the Norwegian ambassador to Britain, a leader in the League of Nations (the ideological forerunner to the United Nations), and won the Nobel Peace prize in 1922. The other hero, Hjalmar Johansen, joined Roald Amundsen on his expedition to the South Pole (1910–12). During that trip he fell out with Amundsen and committed suicide on his return to Norway in 1913. The sea channel between the Svalbard archipelago and Greenland was named the Fram Strait in honour of the famous polar research ship.

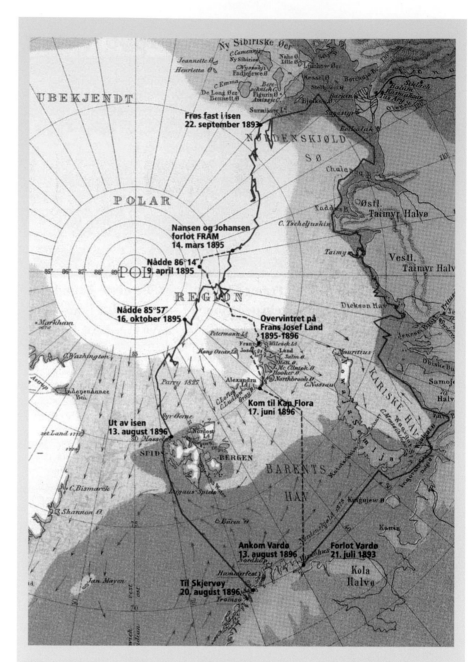

Figure 3.6 The voyage of the *Fram* (solid line) and route of Nansen and Johansen (dashed line) during their expedition of 1893–96

Winds, ocean currents and flow from rivers can all carry pollutants from their source to the Arctic. On a ***stereographic plot***, the routes of wind-borne contaminants from the warmer, populated areas of Earth to the cooler, Arctic are clear (Figure 3.7). These winds can transport contaminants to the

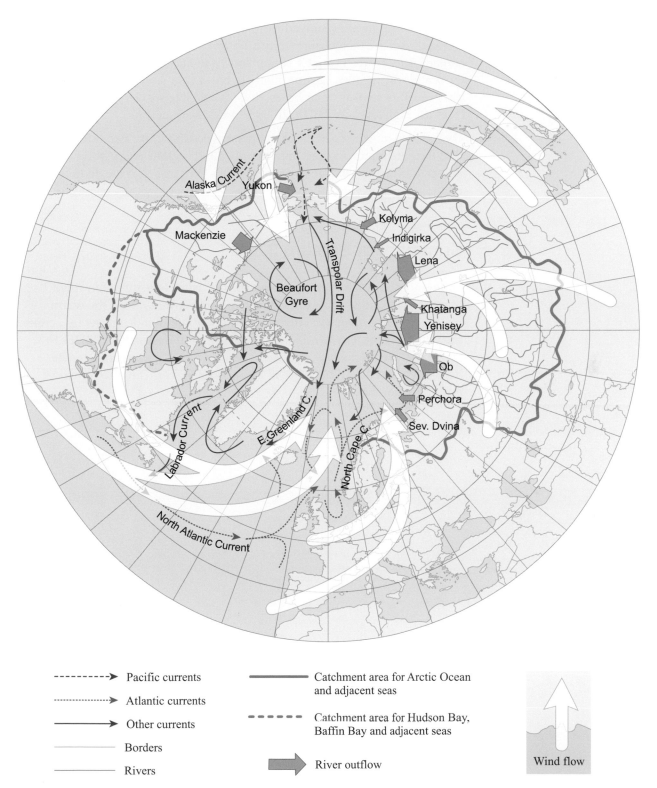

Figure 3.7 Transportation pathways for persistent organic pollutants (POPs) to the Arctic. Note the curving path of the wind currents caused by the rotation of the Earth. (*Source: adapted from Macdonald et al., 2005*)

poles, where they are removed from the atmosphere most likely through snowfall and are then absorbed by animals, perhaps through direct contact. The North Atlantic Current shown in Figure 3.7 flows directly past the waters off western Europe, likely to be a major source of PBDEs. For top predators such as polar bears, there is also likely to be bioaccumulation from the high levels of PBDEs in their prey, the seals.

Overall, the toxicity of POPs to the polar wildlife is not clear, but the fact that they are manufactured only in populated regions and yet can be detected in Arctic wildlife is striking. POPs give us a graphic demonstration that a region once thought of as remote is clearly physically connected to the rest of the planet.

Summary of Section 3

Differences between the albedo and specific heat capacity of terrains mean that they heat up at different rates. Air in contact with the warm terrain rises in convection currents, and horizontal winds are set up across the whole planet. The winds can transport pollutants such as PBDEs to the Arctic, where they are deposited in snowfall and as a result can be detected in Arctic wildlife. Ocean currents and rivers can also transport pollution into the Arctic.

The ice time machine

4

Greenland snowfall differs depending on whether it falls in summer (when snow is comparatively warm and moist) or winter (when snow is cold and dry). These differences mean that as the snow is turned to ice, annual layers are formed that are in many ways similar to tree rings: thick annual layers mean high snowfall and thin annual layers low snowfall. The accumulation of snowfall on the summit of Greenland – and most importantly what is trapped within the crystals as it turns to ice – can provide a record of the past. Digging down into the ice cap is equivalent to going back in time through the snowfall of previous years. Remember from Part 2 that one would have to go down a long way (equivalent perhaps to 300 years of snowfall) before reaching the ice. To make the digging back in time easier a drilling rig that extracts *ice cores* about 13 cm in diameter (Figure 3.8 (a)) is used to get to very deep levels. Once extracted, the annual layers in the cores are clear (Figure 3.8(b)). A video on the course DVD shows how ice cores are extracted.

(a)

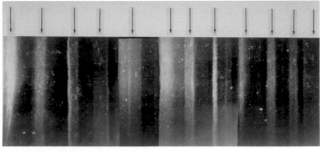

(b)

Figure 3.8 (a) The GISP ice camp on the summit of the Greenland ice cap; (b) snow layers from a Greenland ice core. The arrows show successive years of snowfall.

As well as looking at snowfall, the use of different chemical and physical techniques on ice cores can tell us about dust in the atmosphere, past volcanic activity – and even the industrial production of civilisations long past. For example, Figure 3.9 shows the concentrations of lead in the ice of different ages, and compares it with the recorded production of lead.

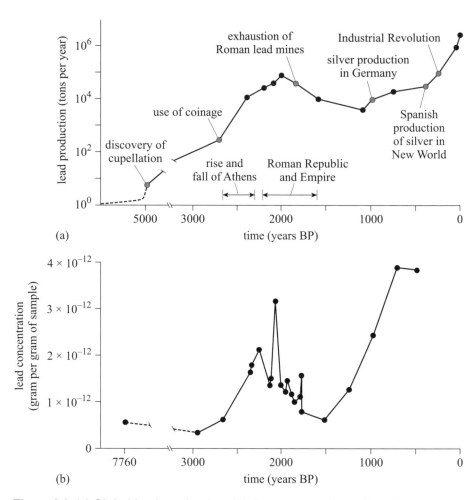

Figure 3.9 (a) Global lead production; (b) the concentration of lead in a Greenland ice core *(Source: adapted from Hong et al., 1994)*

Study note: powers of ten and scientific notation

Figure 3.9(a) shows the production of lead in tonnes multiplied by different powers of ten (10^0, 10^2, etc.). When you see numbers written down it is quite easy to read and understand them when they have few digits, for example 0.01, 0.5, 4, 15, or 132. But when numbers have a lot of digits, for example a small number like 0.0000067, or a very large number like 1700000000, they are less easy to read, and consequently it is harder to understand what they are telling you.

For example, if I ask you to say '75 kg' you would probably respond immediately 'seventy-five kilograms'. But if I asked you to say the mass 330000000 tonnes I am sure you would have to start counting the zeros. To make large and small numbers easier to comprehend we use a system based on what we call powers of ten. In this case the power is the number of tens that are multiplied together. For example, 10^2, which we would say as 'ten to the power of 2', means that two tens are multiplied together. So:

$$10^2 = 10 \times 10 = 100$$

Similarly,

$$10^3 = 10 \times 10 \times 10 = 1000$$

And so on; for example:

$$10^7 = 10 \times 10 \times 10 \times 10 \times 10 \times 10 \times 10 = 10\,000\,000$$

10^7 is easier to understand than 10000000. Note that 10^1 implies just one ten, that is, $10^1 = 10$, so we do not add the power 1 in this case. When dealing with powers of 10 you could also just say that the power is the number of zeros after the 1, so 10^0 is just the number 1.

That covers numbers greater than 1, but what about numbers less than 1 such as 0.1? In powers of ten it would be written as 1 divided by 10, so

$$\frac{1}{10} = 0.1$$

and this is written as 10^{-1}.

Similarly, 10^{-4} is 1 divided by 10 four times:

$$10^{-4} = \frac{1}{10 \times 10 \times 10 \times 10} = 0.0001$$

So how would you write the number 150 as a power of 10? The number 150 is $1.5 \times 10 \times 10$, so would be written 1.5×10^2. This form of writing numbers is known as **scientific notation**. A number written in scientific notation always looks like this:
(number between 1 and 10) $\times 10^{\text{some power}}$.

SAQ 3.2   Taking readings from a graph

From the graph in Figure 3.9, what was the maximum global lead production in tonnes per year before the Industrial Revolution?

When did this occur, and what was the lead concentration in the Greenland ice core at this time?

Graphs can both reveal and conceal information. It is important that you look closely at the axes to make sure that you understand what is being plotted, and on what scale. Some graphs just show what the author believes is the general trend in changes in value; others may show individual points, with or without connecting lines. Where connecting lines are drawn, as in Figure 3.9(b), the effect may be to lead your eyes to think that an isolated point is more important than it really is. The visual impact of a graph is both a strength and a weakness!

Extracting lead from its ores, and to a lesser extent working the lead into pipes etc. (the word 'plumbing' derives directly from the Latin for lead, *plumbum*, as does its chemical symbol, Pb) results in discharge of lead-rich dust to the atmosphere. Given the pattern of wind movements shown in Figure 3.7, it is therefore not surprising that lead should appear in the precipitation over the Arctic for the corresponding period.

4.1 The past temperature of the planet

Measuring the concentration of lead in the ice is called a direct measurement: the ice sample is melted and the water produced contains a very small but readily measured quantity of lead dust. A very accurate set of scales would be needed to measure it, but it is a directly measured quantity. There are also many indirect measurements that can be made using *proxy data*. The concept for using proxies is both simple and brilliant: one measured property allows inference about other states of the system (Box 3.3).

Box 3.3   Proxies

Proxy data occur when scientists measure one, two or even several direct quantities and use these values to infer some other quantity. For example, if I measure my waistline, my weight and my height every week for a year there would be a data set consisting of three variables measured 52 times over the course of a year. They are called variables because they are varying quantities; in this case they vary with time. Typical results would be like those shown in Figure 3.10.

Because I have stopped growing my height does not change throughout the year so, as in the top panel of Figure 3.10, the graph would be a flat line. However, both my waistline and weight do vary. With my body shape, when my weight goes up it all goes on to my waistline, so both the graph of my waistline and the graph of my weight vary in the same way. As my waistline gets bigger I get heavier. The opposite also applies – when my weight goes down my waistline reduces. Because my waistline and weight seem to vary together we say the two variables are **correlated**. In this case they are positively correlated because when my waistline gets bigger, so does my weight. If, for some strange reason, as my waistline got bigger my weight decreased (not a likely scenario!) then the two variables are said to be negatively correlated.

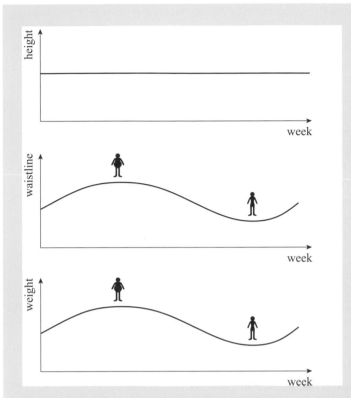

Figure 3.10 Schematic measurements of height, waistline and weight for the author throughout a year

Because my waistline is positively correlated to my weight, there is a mathematical relation between the two variables. So for example, it might be that when my waistline increased by 2 cm I was 1 kg heavier. If I just gave you the data for my waistline over a year, and my starting weight, you could derive values for my weight over the whole year. This makes my waistline a proxy for my weight. If I then told you that I tended to eat more over Christmas and exercised a lot in the summer, then you could think it reasonable to add dates to the graphs in Figure 3.10. My weight and waistline would then be a proxy for the time of year as well. It is important to understand that correlated variables do not tell us anything about the cause of the observation – they only tell us that the items vary in a particular way. In the example above, clearly the expansion of my waistline is not the cause of my weight changing – it is the result of it. A more extreme example of this is that the number of people in the British armed forces has decreased since the First World War, and at the same time global atmospheric temperatures have risen. Whilst these two variables are negatively correlated there is no physical mechanism for one influencing or controlling the other.

I noted above that because two things are correlated it does not necessarily mean that one causes the other, although in the case of the lead data there is an obvious causal link. What is perhaps not so obvious is that we cannot be sure just by looking at a graph whether two variables are correlated. To be sure that the observations do show correlation, scientists use formal *statistical tests*. The details of these are beyond the scope of this course, but they are essential in scientific investigation. In principle, statistical tests use mathematics to tell us the likelihood that *the results we see occur just by chance*. If the mathematics suggest that the results are indeed just chance, we cannot draw any conclusions from them. If, however, the likelihood of it being just a chance relationship is very small, then we can assume that there really is some repeatable relationship between the two. To use one item as a proxy for others, we therefore need first to be sure that there really is a correlation, according to accepted scientific standards. Observing a correlation should also lead us to look for a plausible mechanism whereby one item could affect the other. In the example of temperature and service personnel given above, such a mechanism is almost totally implausible. Even if the correlation were statistically acceptable, its implausibility would lead a scientist to reject it as being due to chance.

SAQ 3.3 Proxy variables

Do the data in Figure 3.9 suggest that lead production and the concentration of lead in ice cores are correlated, so that one could be used as a proxy for the other?

This process of analysis and checking for plausible mechanisms using proxy data has revolutionised the study of past climates.

For example, a simple ice core proxy for moisture in the atmosphere at the time of deposition would be the thickness of the annual snow layer. A thicker layer would mean more snowfall, so the atmosphere must have been wetter to hold the increased snow before it fell. A thinner annual snow layer would imply the opposite. Block 1 showed the Earth's temperature from an Antarctic ice core. The temperature record was constructed entirely from proxy data using the relative amounts of oxygen-16 and oxygen-18 *isotopes*. The water molecules in the ice have a proportion of all three isotopes of oxygen in them (see the Note below) and it has been shown that the relative amounts of the different isotopes vary depending on the temperature of the oceans at the time the ice was deposited. This fact has led to a most useful proxy technique which uses the amount of oxygen-16 compared with the amount of oxygen-18 in the sample to derive the temperature of past climates. In this case the ratio of the oxygen isotopes is a proxy for the temperature of the planet.

The central part of an atom, which makes up most of its mass, is called the *nucleus*; this is surrounded by an 'electron cloud', which largely determines how the atom reacts with other atoms or *molecules. The nucleus of an atom is made of building blocks called protons and neutrons. The number of protons determines what element the atom actually is (look back at Box 2.1 in Block 1 if you need to remind yourself about elements). An atom with one proton is hydrogen and an atom with eight protons is oxygen. However, the number of neutrons at the centre of an atom can vary. Oxygen exists in its natural state with eight protons and either eight, nine or ten neutrons. Atoms with the same number of protons but different numbers of neutrons are called isotopes. The most abundant oxygen isotope, with eight protons and eight neutrons, is called oxygen-16 (8 protons + 8 neutrons), the oxygen isotope which has eight protons and nine neutrons is oxygen-17 (8 protons + 9 neutrons), and the oxygen isotope which has eight protons and ten neutrons is called oxygen-18 (8 protons + 10 neutrons).*

Throughout this block the focus has been on the Arctic, but because some data from the ice cores tell us about conditions over the entire planet (such as Figure 3.9) I am going to show data from another core, this time from Antarctica. The only reason for this is that the core goes back much further in time than any Greenland one. The particular core I am going to use is called the EPICA (European Project for Ice Coring in Antarctica) – Dome C core. Dome C is currently the longest ice core and it has snow layers going back almost 800 000 years throughout the Quaternary and includes the period when *Homo sapiens* evolved. In fact the EPICA core can be used to reconstruct the temperature more than half a million years before *Homo sapiens* ever walked the Earth (Figure 3.11).

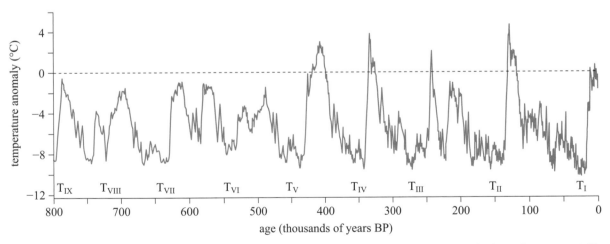

Figure 3.11 The temperature from the EPICA ice core going back to 800 000 years before the present (thousands of years before present or BP). The vertical temperature scale has 0 as the present mean temperature, and goes from –12 °C to +5 °C relative to this.

Figure 3.11 shows that global temperatures have varied considerably, but there also appear to be regular cyclical patterns. At the low points the temperature shown by the core was as much as 10 °C colder than today: colder periods happen about every 100 000 years, with warmer periods between. Four times in the last 450 000 years the intervening warm periods have been warmer than today (up to 4 °C warmer 120 000 years ago). During the nine cold periods shown in Figure 3.11 the snow that fell in winter did not melt in the following summer heat, and the ice sheets grew. What did these temperature variations mean for the rest of the Earth? Other proxy data, such as from sediments found at the bottom of the oceans and lake beds, and the dating of rocks and analysis of ice cores from high-altitude mountain glaciers, show that during the cold periods a large proportion of the northern hemisphere was covered by an ice sheet that was in places several kilometres thick. Glaciers advanced, eroding valleys and mountains, and in the northern hemisphere wildlife moved south to more temperate regions. At the lowest temperatures (Figure 3.12) the ice sheets covered about 10% of the entire planet – up to 30% of all the land.

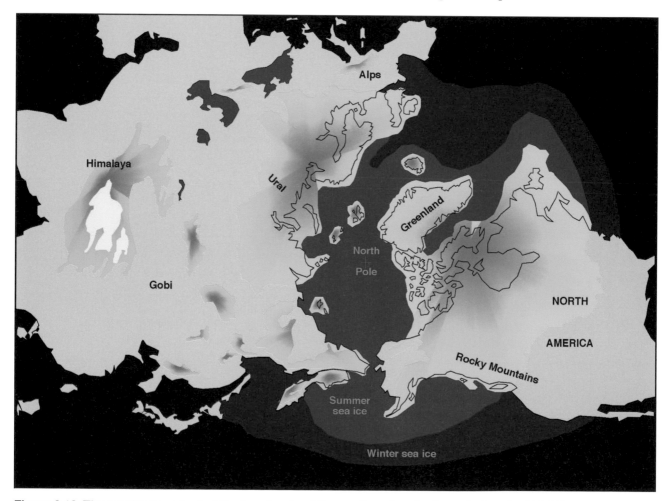

Figure 3.12 The maximum extent of the ice sheets of the northern hemisphere during the 800 000 years of EPICA ice core data. Oceans are coloured dark blue and continents yellow. Ice is shown as lighter shades of blue.

The sea froze as far south as the northern Spanish coast and almost all of Britain was buried beneath the ice. These periods are called the *ice ages*. A vast quantity of water was locked in these ice sheets, so sea level was as much as 120 m lower than today and there was dry land between Britain and the rest of Europe. During times between these cold periods the ice sheets melted and the water from land ice meant that sea levels rose. These are called *interglacials*. Note that it is only the melting of land ice that changes sea levels. As climate change deniers never tire of reminding us, melting sea ice does not change the sea level. Remember that ice is less dense than water, so it floats. As sea ice melts, it forms a smaller volume of water than the volume of ice. In fact, the volume of water formed is exactly the same as the volume of ice that was below the water surface when it was floating, so no change in sea level occurs. Of course, when ice on the land melts and flows into the seas, this does raise sea levels.

SAQ 3.4.   The Arctic defined during an ice age

What would happen to the size of the Arctic, as we have defined it, during an ice age?

Activity 3.2   Rates of change of temperature

Look carefully at the temperature record in Figure 3.11. Are there any general observations you can make about the rates of change of temperature between the relatively warm and the relatively cold periods?

Discussion
The record in Figure 3.11 shows that the temperatures fall relatively slowly but rise relatively quickly – particularly in the most recent 450 000 years.

Assuming (correctly) that the temperature is a proxy for the amount of ice on the planet, the ice sheets in Figure 3.12 took about 100 000 years to grow, and yet they rapidly disappeared – typically in only approximately 10 000 years. Consequently sea levels fall slowly as the ice sheets grow, and rise relatively quickly as they decay again. The obvious question from Figure 3.11 is what causes these regular fluctuations in temperature and ice cover. One of the most influential is the *Milankovitch cycles* of the Earth's orbit.

The amount of energy that the Earth receives from the Sun depends on its distance from the Sun. We tend to assume that this is constant, but in fact the orbit of the Earth around the Sun is an ellipse, with the Sun at one of its foci (Figure 3.13), so the distance from the Earth to the Sun varies over the course of an orbit (one year). If the Sun emits a constant amount of energy, then when the Earth is closer it will receive more than when it is further away. However, the shape of the ellipse also varies with time, and the Earth's axis of rotation also wobbles, like a gyroscope. The Serbian geophysicist Milutin Milanković realised in 1920 that the varying energy received by the Earth as a result of these two factors could be the cause of the ice ages. He showed that the ellipse changes shape over periods of about 100 000 years. The timing of these changes, combined with the wobble in the Earth's rotation, matched up with data he had for the times and durations of the ice ages. He showed that the incoming energy would be at a minimum when there was an ice age and at a maximum during an interglacial. Unfortunately, modern records go back much further than the data to which Milanković had access, and further back in time the match is not so good. Earlier ice ages can be earlier and later than the predictions from Milanković's model. Clearly there are other factors affecting the climate. This story illustrates another aspect of the way that science develops. Milanković's model was tested against new data, and found not to be fully consistent with it. The challenge was then for scientists either to completely reject that model, or to look for other effects that could be combined with the basic model to provide a better explanation of the observations. As we noted at the beginning of Part 2, scientific models are always subject to revision as new data is found.

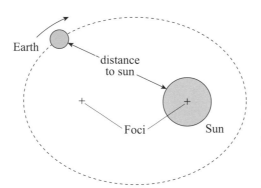

Figure 3.13 **The orbit of the Earth around the Sun is an ellipse, so throughout a year the Earth–Sun distance, and consequently the amount of solar energy received at the surface of the Earth, varies. Note that this picture shows the orbit shape greatly exaggerated.**

4.2 The Keeling Curve revisited

In Block 1 you met the Keeling Curve – the plot showing the trend in rising atmospheric CO_2 concentrations since 1958 recorded at Mauna Loa in Hawaii. The story of atmospheric CO_2 in the last 50 years is a relentless rise derived from human use of hydrocarbons and, as I write this in 2008, the annual mean concentration is 383 parts per million (ppm). When Keeling first collected his CO_2 data he travelled around making the measurements at widely spaced locations – but he saw that apart from the daily and seasonal variation caused by local plant photosynthesis and respiration the concentration was virtually the same wherever he measured it. Keeling quickly realised that this meant it was possible to measure the CO_2 in one location, such as Mauna Loa, and it would be a reference point for the whole planet.

Activity 3.3   How representative is the Keeling curve?

Is Keeling's contention that the Mauna Loa data is a good reference for the whole planet consistent with what you have learned about atmospheric movements?

Discussion
Recall from the discussion of the spread of pollutants by wind (and from your own experience if you live in an exposed area!) that there are constant air movements around the planet. These movements stir up the air and mix it constantly. This constant mixing means that the concentration of CO_2 is likely to be similar all over the globe. This sort of questioning as to whether methods and data are plausible is another good example of scientific method.

After a few years of measurement Keeling must have been astonished to see CO_2 levels rising so rapidly. The problem of course with the Keeling CO_2 data is that it extends only back to 1958. However, ice-core researchers realised that the air bubbles trapped when the ice was formed would contain atmospheric gas samples. As well as giving a proxy record of past temperatures, ice cores can give the exact atmospheric CO_2 concentration for the last 800 000 years.

SAQ 3.5   Direct and proxy measurements

Is measurement of gas trapped in a bubble in an ice core a direct or proxy measurement?

Part 2 showed that that it takes a certain period of time for the bubbles to be closed off and air to be isolated. As a result this method cannot provide a concentration until this has happened. In the case of the Dome C core the most recent atmospheric CO_2 concentration available is from 130 or so years ago. Figure 3.14 shows that over the last nine glacial cycles the CO_2 and temperature appear to be positively and very closely correlated, showing the same patterns of change.

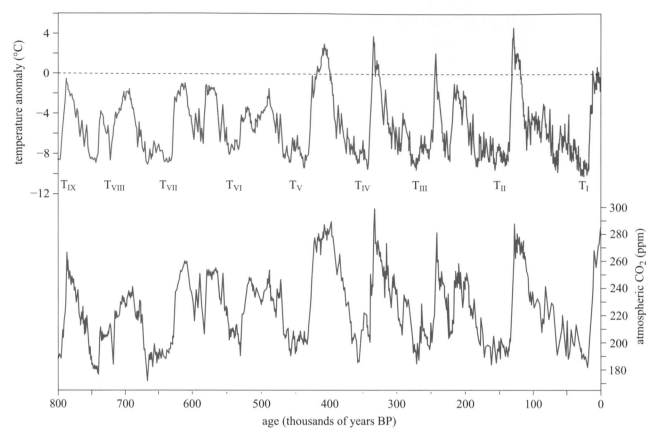

Figure 3.14 Past atmospheric CO$_2$ concentrations and temperatures going back through nine ice ages, taken from the EPICA ice core

---

SAQ 3.6   Temperature and CO$_2$ values

1   According to Figure 3.14, what were the typical CO$_2$ levels during the extreme low-temperature periods (ice ages) and at the height of the warmer interglacials?

2   How does the value of the atmospheric CO$_2$ concentration for 2008 quoted earlier compare with that in the interglacials of the previous nine cycles of the EPICA Dome C ice core?

We now have data that we could possibly use to predict what might happen as a result of the increasing CO$_2$ concentration that Keeling detected. We could theoretically plot a graph of temperature against CO$_2$ concentration and, from this, read off what is the temperature for any given CO$_2$ concentration. Unfortunately, there is a problem with this. The current atmospheric CO$_2$ concentration is higher than at any time in the previous 800 000 years, so even if we had a graph of the mathematical relationship between temperature and CO$_2$ concentration from the earlier data, it would not include the current (and much less, any possible future increased) CO_2 concentration. We would have to extrapolate (that is, extend) the graph beyond the available set of values, and we cannot know for sure that the relationship will hold outside these limits. This means that it is difficult to use information from these earlier periods to predict what may happen in the near future. We are fairly sure that Milankovitch cycles amplified by greenhouse gases are responsible for the coming and going of ice ages; it is our best theory and one to which almost all climate scientists subscribe. But as we have seen, it is not a complete explanation, and some of the earlier cycles do not conform to this theory. To make useful predictions for the near future, and hence to suggest actions to protect our environment, we need to look for some more detailed information and scientific models.

Box 3.4   Prediction, extrapolation and falsification

Much of science is concerned with gathering data, but according to the philosopher of science Karl Popper (1902–94) a key part of scientific method is making testable predictions from the data. According to his model of scientific method, a scientist makes observations about the world, and from these observations constructs theories about the causes of the observed phenomena. Using those theories, the scientist is then able to make predictions as to what might occur in a new, but similar situation to the ones previously observed. The scientist should then set up such a situation, and test whether the observed behaviour does indeed occur. If it does, then the theory is supported. But if the observations do not accord with the theory, then the theory is either inadequate or possibly completely wrong.

The story of Nansen's expedition in the drifting ice is a spectacular example of this. From the observation that trees from Siberia turned up in Svalbard, he predicted that a ship trapped in the ice would follow the same path. He then proceeded to test this theory in a very practical, but dangerous way.

This continual attempt to test, and potentially falsify, theories is regarded as the essential feature of scientific method that distinguishes it from other approaches. An artist or a journalist may want to present their interpretation of a situation, but this interpretation is only descriptive, not predictive. Some religions and similar codes make predictions and suggestions about what should happen, but these are rarely tested.

Summary of Section 4

The ice cores in Greenland and Antarctica currently provide a direct record of the snowfall going back almost 800 000 years. As snow falls, impurities such as lead are trapped in the ice, and so ice cores can give direct measurements of past atmospheric concentrations. By using isotope proxies such as oxygen-16 and oxygen-18, ice cores can be used to estimate atmospheric temperatures. Over the time period of the cores the Earth has gone through nine cyclical temperature variations with a cold period (ice age) approximately every 100 000 years. Trapped gases within the ice cores allow a direct measurement of atmospheric CO_2 concentration and throughout the entire Dome C record, temperature and the greenhouse gas CO_2 are positively correlated. Milankovitch cycles caused by variations in the Earth's orbit, amplified by greenhouse gases, are the best current theory for the cause of ice ages, but these do not provide a sufficiently accurate model to predict the near future course of atmospheric change.

The end of the last ice age: the Holocene

5

I have already noted that the great ice sheets took about 100 000 years to form and only about 10 000 years to decay. So what happened at the end of the last ice age? Figure 3.15 shows the EPICA ice core CO_2 concentration and air temperature for the most recent 20 000 years, which is within the last ice age. The temperature scale shows the difference from the average temperature of the last 1000 years, so 0 °C is no change from today's climate.

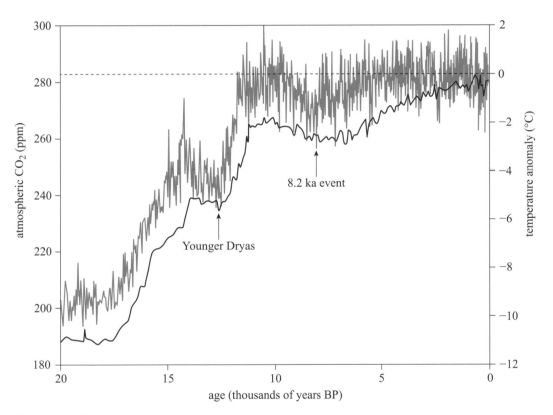

Figure 3.15 The atmospheric CO_2 concentration (relatively smooth line) and air temperature anomaly (spiky line) at the EPICA ice core in Antarctica over the last 20 000 years

Figure 3.15 shows again the high correlation between the two variables: 20 000 years ago it was up to 10 °C colder and CO_2 concentration was about 200 ppm lower than today. Over the most recent 10 000 years atmospheric temperature has been within about 2 °C of current temperatures (see Block 1 Section 3.3.2) and this climatically stable time period is called the

Holocene. Figure 3.14 shows that such a warm, stable period has been very unusual in the last 800 000 years, yet it is only during the Holocene that agriculture and civilisations have developed. *Homo sapiens* has flourished in the stable climate era. Figure 3.15 shows that up to approximately 14 000 years ago the planet appeared to be leaving the ice age, and the temperature rose to within 1 °C of the 0 °C line. But then there was a very rapid cooling of 4–5 °C (and most of this in just a couple of decades) and lower temperatures resumed from 12 900 to 11 600 years before the present. This cold period affected most of the planet and is called the Younger Dryas, after a pretty Arctic alpine flowering plant called the white dryas (Figure 3.16). This species spread its geographical range as temperatures fell and the tundra *biome* expanded in area.

Figure 3.16 The white dryas. The Latin name of this pretty flower is *Dryas octopetala* (meaning dryas flower with eight petals – although it can have up to 16 petals).

Another interesting event shown in Figure 3.15 happened just before 8000 years ago (called the '8.2 ka event' where ka is an abbreviation meaning 1000 years), when there was a clear but relatively small temperature and CO_2 decrease which was associated with drier conditions in some parts of the world. This represents the largest climatic variation that civilisation has currently had to cope with. So what happened in the Younger Dryas and 8000 years ago to make the planet suddenly colder? The changes occurred too fast for the Milankovitch cycle to be responsible. We now believe that the only way to cause that much cooling is by a sudden change in part of the global ocean circulation. Just as there are global patterns of air circulation, so there are also much slower, but enormous, movements of water around the oceans, driven by changes in water temperature and salinity (Box 3.5).

Box 3.5   Wally Broecker's great ocean conveyor belt

The density of fresh water decreases as its temperature rises above 4 °C. The density of salt water in the oceans likewise depends on temperature, but also on the amount of salt within it. In the seas of the North Atlantic Ocean the surface waters are cooler than the lower layers and so they sink. In contrast, in places like the central Pacific Ocean the relatively dry, warm air increases evaporation and the surface waters are both warm and salty. All around the planet different regional climatic conditions create surface waters with different densities. Because the denser waters sink, over time horizontal currents are set up similar to the processes for the winds. The result is a vast, three-dimensional circulation across the entire ocean. In the 1980s the American climate scientist Wallace Broecker suggested that the global ocean circulation could be viewed as analogous to a conveyor belt that moved heat and salt around the planet. Broecker's schematic picture (Figure 3.17) has become one of the iconic images of climate science.

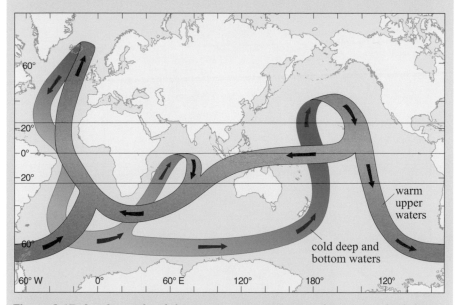

Figure 3.17 A schematic of the great ocean conveyor that moves both heat and salt around the planet

It is a huge simplification, but on a global scale Broecker's conveyor belt is excellent at helping us understand planetary processes such as the Younger Dryas and the 8.2 ka event.

Heat that is carried in the ocean conveyor past Britain and up the coast of Norway towards Svalbard both keeps the UK climate warmer and moister than it would otherwise be and also means that the ice edge is a long way north compared with similar latitudes in North America (Figure 3.18).

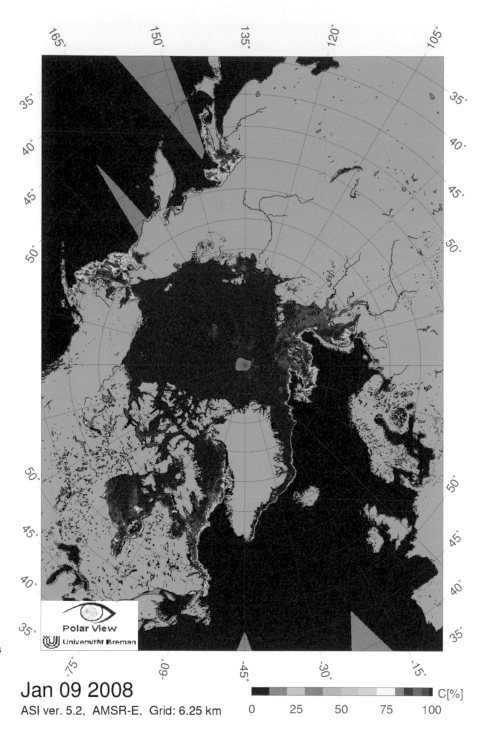

Figure 3.18 Sea ice concentration (the amount of the ocean covered by ice measured as a percentage) measured by satellite on 9 January 2008. Purple colours are almost continuous ice cover and the blue colours represent open water. Land is green.

Jan 09 2008
ASI ver. 5.2, AMSR-E, Grid: 6.25 km

One way to cool the planet, as occurred in the Younger Dryas or the 8.2 ka event, is to stop the ocean conveyor carrying the heat northwards. It is believed that this indeed happened as a result of large quantities of melt water from the North American continental ice sheets flooding into the north Atlantic and changing the surface density of the ocean. Once the conveyor was stopped, the climate was plunged into a cold period. Although similar events seem to have occurred further back in time, the

Younger Dryas and the 8.2 ka events may have been particularly significant for human civilisation. The earliest dated human settlements are in the Mediterranean about 13 000 years ago – in the middle of the Younger Dryas. It is interesting to compare the spread of human civilisation across the Middle East and Europe (Figure 3.19) with the temperature data

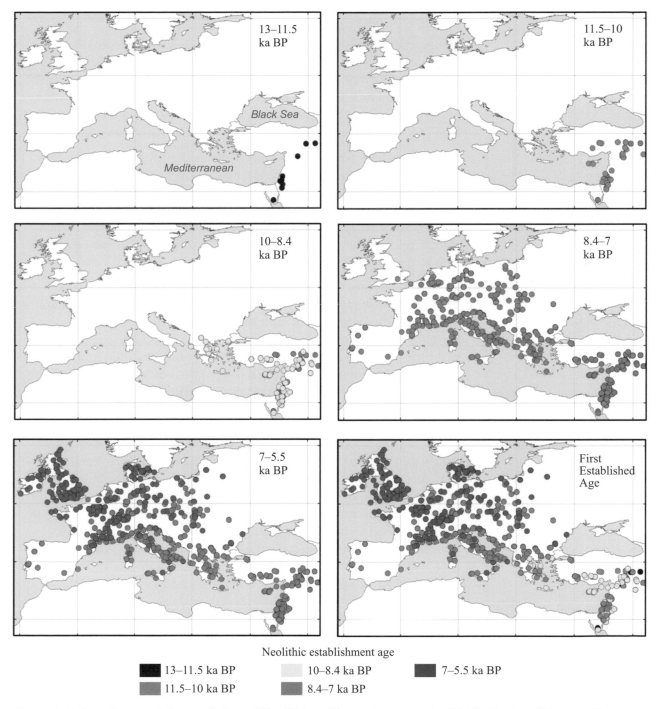

Figure 3.19 Locations and dates of sites of Neolithic settlements across the Middle East and Europe. The coloured dots indicate new sites that were established during each time period; grey dots represent pre-existing sites established during earlier time periods. *(Source: Turney and Brown, 2007)*

of Figure 3.15. During the first 5000 years of human civilisation, from 13 ka BP to 8.4 ka BP, settlements are concentrated on the shores of the Mediterranean and Black Sea. However, after the 8.2 ka event and the collapse of the North American ice sheets, the flooding of fresh water into the Atlantic that stopped the conveyor also caused a rapid sea-level rise of over 1.4 m and large-scale flooding. After this date the settlements rapidly spread northwards.

The exact driving factor for this human migration is impossible to determine, but it is interesting that it seemed to begin immediately after the 8.2 ka climate event. This event may even have been the main factor in the migration and an example of the effects of climate change that our society will have to cope with. Unfortunately we do not have available the empty land of 8000 years ago.

In recent decades our understanding of the reality of climate change has moved from one of slow and gradual change over deep time to clear evidence that there have been naturally occurring climate changes of several degrees Celsius and sea-level jumps of over 1 m within timescales of a decade or so. In fact, the very latest research on the Younger Dryas using Greenland ice core data has revealed that central Greenland cooled by a staggering 2–4 °C in just 1–3 years!

While the Younger Dryas and the 8.2 ka event were entirely natural, Block 1 established that today there is an additional human contribution to consider. But when exactly did the human contribution begin? Often the phrase 'pre-industrial levels' is used to mean 'before significant anthropogenic changes started', but it is not specific. Could humans have influenced the climate before the Industrial Revolution of the eighteenth century? Block 1 noted that another very significant greenhouse gas is methane (CH_4), and 1 cubic metre of methane in the atmosphere can be over 25 times more effective at trapping heat than the same amount of CO_2. Past atmospheric methane concentrations can also be directly measured from ice cores. Over the last quarter of a million years, CH_4 concentration and the variation of solar radiation reaching the Earth attributed to the Milankovitch cycle are positively correlated (Figure 3.20). But this correlation dramatically breaks down in the most recent data of the Holocene. The latest 5000 years of methane data show that the atmospheric concentration has risen dramatically out of synchrony with the solar radiation. The most recent ice core data has a concentration as high as any period in the entire ice core record, at over 700 ppb (parts per billion). Carbon dioxide has a similar break from the expected downward trend although starting earlier at about 8000 years ago.

If the 'normal' trend of methane and carbon dioxide was downwards, along with the Milankovitch cycle, then where have the extra gases come from?

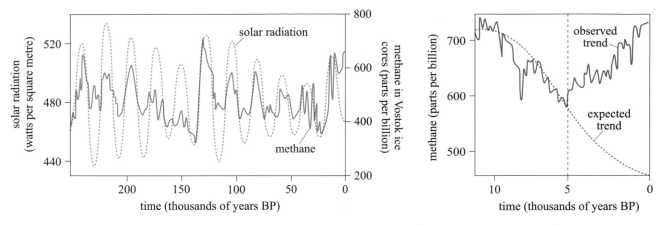

Figure 3.20 (a) The atmospheric concentration of methane and solar radiation reaching the Earth's surface, from the Milankovitch cycle; (b) observed and expected atmospheric methane levels over the last 11 000 years

Carbon dioxide and methane are by-products of our civilisation, and in the words of the climate scientist William Ruddiman,

> Human activities tied to farming – primarily agricultural deforestation and crop irrigation – must have added the extra CO_2 and methane to the atmosphere.

(Ruddiman, 2005)

As with CO_2, since the Industrial Revolution the atmospheric concentration of methane has more than doubled and currently is over 1700 ppb. Virtually all of that rise has been from anthropogenic sources, including major food production activities such as rice and cattle production. Not only were humans possibly affected by climate change during the Holocene, but we had also started our impact on the planet thousands of years before the Egyptian pyramids were built. How then are these changes being seen today?

SAQ 3.7   Recent climates

How does the Earth's climate over the last 10 000 years compare with that of previous times, and what does this mean for humans in the future?

Summary of Section 5

Since the end of the last ice age the climate has been uncharacteristically stable compared with the previous 800 000 years of the ice core record. This stable period is called the Holocene. The change from ice age to interglacial was not smooth and there were two rapid cooling periods: the Younger Dryas and the 8.2 ka event. These are the most significant climate changes that humans have had to endure and both have been linked to changes in the global ocean circulation. The 8.2 ka event coincided with the start of the spread of human settlement throughout Europe. By 5000 years ago there is clear evidence of human influence on the composition of the atmosphere.

6 The contemporary Arctic climate

There is a remarkable seasonality in the Arctic climate. For example, the flow in some of the great rivers of Russia and North America that empty into the Arctic Ocean almost stops in winter (Figure 3.21). During May, ice in the rivers starts to break and in June there is a rapid flood of fresh water followed by a fall in flow until November, when it freezes.

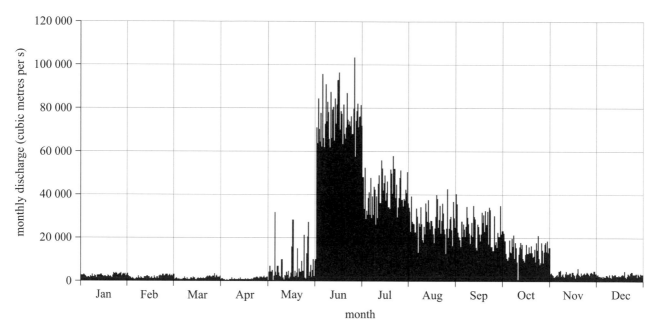

Figure 3.21 The monthly discharge on the Lena River (Russia). Each individual bar in the graph represents a monthly value for each year during 1935–1999.

A similar huge seasonal signal is seen in the Arctic sea ice cover (Figures 1.14 and 1.15). Most people are surprised to realise that the sea ice of the frozen Arctic Ocean is only a few metres thick. Beneath this is a few kilometres of water (Figure 1.13). In winter as much as 16 million square kilometres of the ocean freezes, and as this melts in summer only about 6 million square kilometres remains frozen (Figure 3.22). The seasonal variation of almost 10 million square kilometres is equivalent to about 45 times the area of the United Kingdom.

The contemporary Arctic climate appears to be changing. However, average global temperatures mask regional variations and the Arctic has been warming faster than the global mean (Figure 3.23).

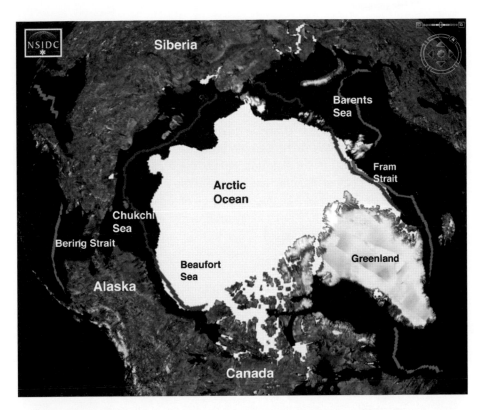

Figure 3.22 The ice cover of the Arctic Ocean in September 2005. The average ice extent for September (when ice area is at a minimum) for the period 1979–2000 is shown as a red line and the average ice extent for March (when the ice area is at its maximum) is shown as a blue line.

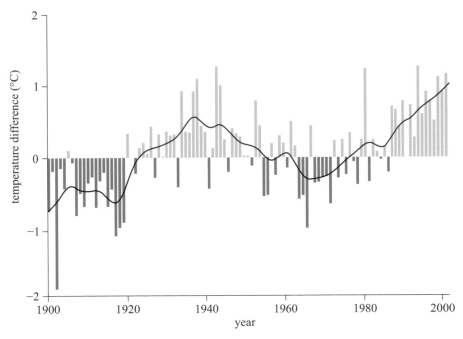

Figure 3.23 The annual average near surface temperature from all weather stations on land relative to the average for 1961–1990 for all regions from 60° N to 90° N (*Source: Arctic Climate Impact Assessment, 2005*)

Activity 3.4   Recent climate change in the Arctic

Describe the changes in Arctic temperature that are shown in Figure 3.23.

Discussion

With the exception of a period in the 1960s and 70s the Arctic temperature has been above the 1961–1990 average in most years since 1920. Currently the temperature is about 1 °C above the mean temperature for 1961–1990. This data came from the Arctic Climate Impact Assessment. They appear to use the latitude of 60° N as their definition of the Arctic, so Figure 3.23 must include meteorological stations that are not in the Arctic as we have defined it, and are less likely to be affected directly by changing ice and snow cover. For this reason Figure 3.23 most likely underestimates the temperature increase – but what is its impact?

Figure 3.24 compares the surface melting on the Greenland ice cap in 1992 and 2005 as measured by satellite. Part 2 of this block noted that for ice to form, the snow has to survive the following summer. But an increasing area of the Greenland ice cap is melting in summer so annual snow layers are not being converted to ice in these regions.

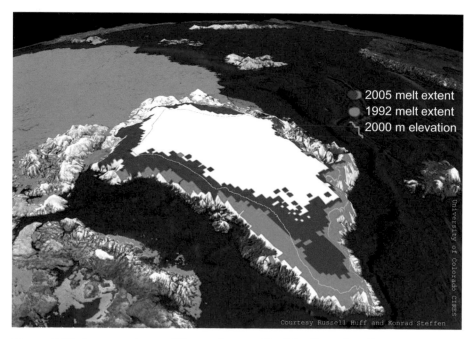

Figure 3.24 A comparison of the surface melt of the Greenland ice cap in 1992 and 2005

It is an extremely complex process to estimate the melt of the whole ice cap, and the current best value is that Greenland is melting in the range 90–250 billion tonnes of ice per year. All of this melt is contributing to the predicted sea-level rise of at least 1–2 m by 2100, and a rise of only 1 m would affect well over 100 million people worldwide. The fresh water from the ice cap could also slow Broecker's conveyor (Box 3.5), causing other climate impacts.

For the Arctic sea ice the signal of climate change is clear: it is getting thinner and the amount of it that survives the summer is reducing. Figure 3.25 shows the trend in extent of sea ice in September (the summer minimum, the mean of which is shown as the red line in Figure 3.22). The sea ice minimum is decreasing at a rate of almost 9% per decade. This means that approximately 100 000 square kilometres less of the ocean is covered by sea ice each year. In 2007 the September ice area was only about 4 million square kilometres (off the bottom of the scale in Figure 3.25!); by September 2008 the minimum was slightly higher but still off the scale. I would be interested in what the latest September value is as you are reading this.

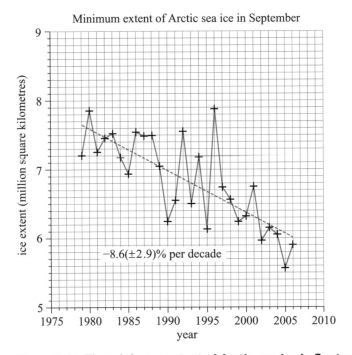

Figure 3.25 The minimum extent of Arctic sea ice in September of each year from 1979 to 2006. There is a consistent trend downwards. More recent data for 2007 and 2008 is off the scale.

Activity 3.5   The changing mean albedo

What is likely to be the effect of these changes in ice cover on the albedo of the Arctic region?

Discussion

Recall from Table 3.1 that the albedo of open water is 3% and that of sea ice is 40%. So the increased thawing during summer will decrease the albedo, so that less energy will be reflected back into space, and more energy will be absorbed.

The effect of this on the albedo is actually more complex than suggested by Activity 3.5, but this ice–albedo *feedback* loop (Figure 3.26) is potentially very important. Table 3.1 gives the average albedo of sea ice as approximately 40%. Sea ice is complex and it could consist of a mixture of bare ice, ice with snow on (the snow could be either wet or dry) or even ponds of freshwater on the ice as it melts, and each one of these types has a different albedo. As temperatures rise there will be more bare ice, melt ponds and open water and the overall albedo will decrease. This means that less energy will be reflected, so more solar energy is absorbed by the ocean, causing further warming and ice melting. The ice–ocean system is in a *positive feedback* loop and changes such as melting ice naturally lead to more melting ice.

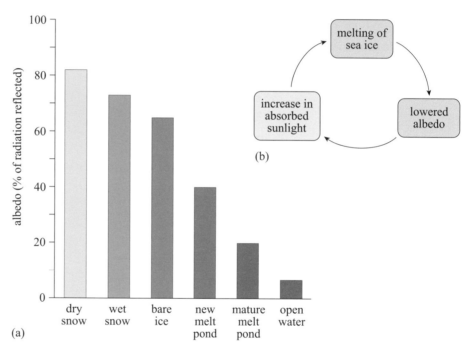

Figure 3.26 The ice–albedo feedback loop: (a) graph of the albedo of various ice categories and open water; (b) an increase in absorbed sunlight leads ice melting which lowers the albedo, causing more sunlight to be absorbed

Box 3.6   Positive and negative feedback

Feedback is the term that is used to describe the situation where the output from a process affects the input to that process. You may have encountered the 'howl' that can occur when a microphone is placed too near a loudspeaker; the sound from the loudspeaker feeds back to the microphone, gets amplified and fed back again so that the volume of sound keeps on increasing until the amplifier overloads. This is an example of positive feedback. Populations of organisms can exhibit the same effect.

If one generation produces more than one surviving offspring per adult, there are more organisms to produce young in the next generation, who produce more young in the next, and so on. This leads to a population explosion. Economic growth is supposed to work the same way – increased wealth this year allows us to spend and invest to produce more wealth next year, to produce more wealth the next year, etc. Of course, the sound from the loudspeaker cannot get louder and louder forever, populations of organisms don't actually go on expanding forever and, whatever economists may tell us, economic growth is unlikely to continue unchecked. The sound from the speaker is limited by the power available to the amplifier and populations can be limited by their food supply. These limits can either have an effect like running into a brick wall, or they can be more subtle. The subtler version is the phenomenon of *negative feedback*, where an increase in the output from the process causes the process itself to 'slow down', so that output returns to a lower level. Populations are a classic example. As there are more organisms present, there is likely to be less food available per individual (or the increased population may attract more predators), so that the rate of production of young decreases and the population tends to stabilise. Negative feedback is a fundamental concept in the control of machinery and electronic devices, and there are many other examples from ecosystems. Maybe economists should spend some time studying control engineering!

Many climate models suggest that, given the predictions of Arctic warming, the sea ice may disappear completely in summer sometime around 2060. But given the observations of the last few years, I could not put the current situation any better than this recent article:

> With sharply rising atmospheric greenhouse gas concentrations, the change to a seasonally ice-free Arctic Ocean seems inevitable. The only question is how fast we get there. The emerging view is that if we're still waiting for the rapid slide towards this ice-free state, we won't be waiting much longer.

(Serreze and Stroeve, 2008)

The extent of snow cover in the northern hemisphere is decreasing in a similar way in another positive feedback loop, but what about the frozen ground beneath the snow that is called *permafrost*? Most of the global permafrost is in the Arctic and high mountain areas (Figure 3.27) and many cities use the frozen ground as foundations for building – and even for temporary roads in winter. It should be expected that the area of permafrost will decrease, but it is difficult to measure. Virtually all boreholes into the permafrost show that Arctic warming (Figure 3.23) is penetrating into the ground. While frozen, permafrost provides a solid surface – a vehicle will

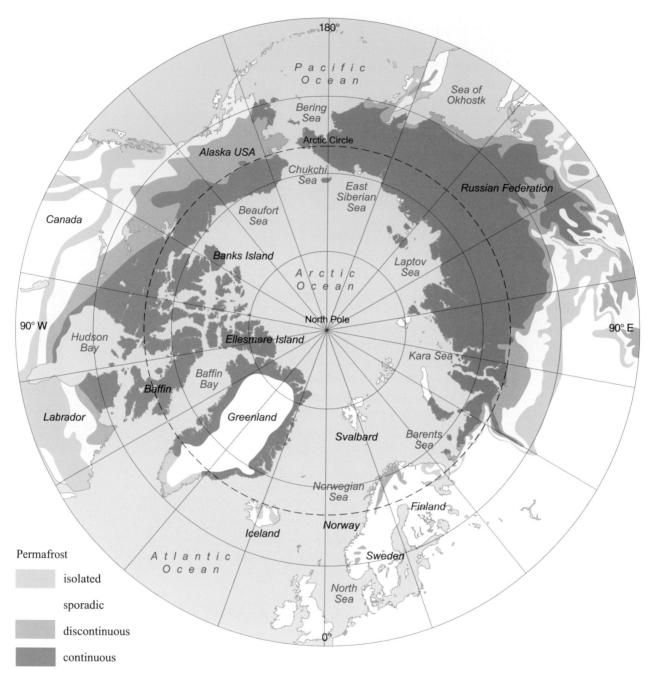

Figure 3.27 The permafrost distribution in the northern hemisphere. The largest area of continuous permafrost is in the Arctic and high mountain areas.

leave no trace. As it melts the situation is different. The State of Alaska has strict rules for vehicle travel on permafrost to prevent environmental damage. When it is too warm, travel is not allowed. The duration of allowed permafrost travel set by the Alaska Department of Natural Resources is an interesting climate change proxy! (Figure 3.28). In the last 25 years the number of days on which oil exploration is allowed on the tundra has more than halved.

The retreat of the permafrost is serious. Building foundations are collapsing and there are 'drunken forests' as land beneath trees melts, subsides and slumps. Building should only be done on carefully built foundations and the Trans-Alaska Pipeline was even built on refrigerated pillars to prevent pipe fracture through permafrost thaw subsidence.

Figure 3.28 **The annual duration of allowed tundra travel for oil exploration activities set by the Alaska Department of Natural Resources**

There is, however, another more worrying problem as the permafrost retreats. As the ground subsides the depressions usually form lakes because the melt water cannot flow through the frozen ground beneath. Thawing of the permafrost at the lake bottom releases organic matter perhaps 30–40 000 years old into the water. The organic matter decomposes, giving off methane – a potent global warming gas. The permafrost–methane feedback cycle is another positive feedback in the system (Figure 3.29).

Figure 3.29 **While permafrost retreat could be perceived as a less glamorous area of climate research, the positive methane feedback cycle means that it is a profoundly important climate issue**

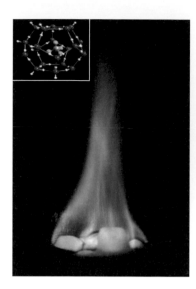

Figure 3.30 Burning methane released from methane clathrate. Inset is the crystal structure: the methane molecule (green) is trapped within the ice molecules (red).

Another potentially significant source of methane in the Arctic is trapped in the shallow seabed of the Arctic Ocean and is called *methane clathrate*. This is ice with methane trapped within the crystal matrix (Figure 3.30). As the ocean warms, the release of large quantities of methane into the atmosphere from clathrates would be yet another positive feedback, but it is currently unquantifiable as there is not even a basic understanding of the distribution and amount in the Arctic. This has been called the *clathrate gun hypothesis* and it could lead to a runaway greenhouse effect that may have happened before in deep time. It could even have been responsible for the mass animal extinctions described in Block 1.

SAQ 3.8   Arctic feedbacks

What is the particular importance of feedback processes in the context of climate, particularly with respect to the Arctic?

It is ironic that anthropogenic climate change driving sea ice and permafrost retreat means that more oil, coal and gas fields are becoming accessible (Figure 1.38).

I shall leave the last word at the same point as I started this part: *Ursus maritimus* – the sea bear. Figure 3.1 showed the area used by one polar bear and computer models can predict the effects of anthropogenic climate change on these areas. The story is complex but the message is stark and clear. The bear habitats will decrease in extent in the near future. It may soon be possible to see bears only in northern Greenland and the Canadian archipelago. Whether you believe this is an issue of concern depends on both your moral and political opinions. The evidence of change is too clear to ignore. If you decide that as a remote region the Arctic is not relevant then it could be that you are missing the point. The positive feedbacks and global environmental flows mean that the Arctic will not only be a victim of climate change but a source for some of the changes that we may have to adapt to, such as rising sea levels from the melting Greenland ice cap. It is therefore possibly more than just a barometer of global change.

To be more literate, the Jacobean poet John Donne wrote in the seventeenth century, before the Arctic was mapped,

> No man is an island, entire of itself; every man is a piece of the continent, a part of the main ... never send to know for whom the bell tolls; it tolls for thee.

(Donne, Meditation XVII, 1624)

Summary of Section 6

The Arctic climate is strongly seasonal and many processes such as river flow virtually stop in winter. However, the region is warming – more than 1 °C since 1900 – and this is affecting everything. The area of the Greenland ice cap that is melting is increasing and the melt water will contribute to global sea-level rise. The amount of sea ice in summer is consistently decreasing due to both increasing temperatures and also the positive ice–albedo feedback loop. A summer ice-free Arctic is certain, and the only question is how soon it will be. The permafrost is in all probability retreating in extent, causing problems both for buildings and for the natural environment. An additional consequence is that the permafrost is releasing methane which, through positive feedback, may yet cause a runaway greenhouse effect.

Summary of Part 3

In this part I have presented evidence showing that even apparently remote regions of our planet are intimately connected through physical processes. For example, once an organic POP is transported to the poles, then biological processes can take over and through bioaccumulation perhaps cause harm. But this physical connection has allowed the ice to preserve unique proxy records of the past climate of our planet. Directly measuring the gases trapped in the ice has enabled histories of past atmospheric CO_2 and methane concentrations to be compiled, and we now know that the current atmospheric CO_2 concentration is higher than at any time in the last million years. It is stunning to think that human civilisation has only happened over the last 10 000 years, when the ice cores show that the climate has been uncharacteristically stable. However, humans have been affecting the climate for at least half of that time and the Arctic is now warming at a higher rate than almost all of the rest of the planet. Observations show that there are already significant regional changes that humans and animals will have to adapt to. Through feedback processes these regional changes will affect us all.

After completing Part 3 you should be able to:

- appreciate how chemical processes in the rest of the world affect the Arctic environment and the species inhabiting it
- recognise the physical processes that determine atmosphere and oceanic flows in the Arctic
- appreciate the scientific research process and the use of scientific evidence
- use quantitative scientific evidence to examine the link between atmospheric carbon dioxide levels and global temperatures
- recognise how scientific data is used to predict global climatic change
- recognise the role (and limitations?) of scientific data in attempting to predict global climatic change.

Answers to SAQs

SAQ 3.1

If the same amount of energy reaches a desert and a frozen sea, the amount of energy available to heat up the material will be the same, because Table 3.1 shows us that the two substances have the same albedo – 40%. In both cases the amount of energy available to heat up the material will be:

$$\text{amount of energy} = 100\% - 40\% = 60\%$$

So 60% of the incoming energy will be available to heat up the material.

If snow falls on the sea ice, then its albedo will increase from 40% to 80–90% and so the amount of energy available to heat up the ice will be:

$$\text{amount of energy} = 100\% - 90\% = 10\%$$

Only 10% of the incoming energy is now available to heat up the ice, and almost all of the incident energy is reflected away. Clearly the albedo is extremely important for the polar regions.

SAQ 3.2

The peak in global lead production before the Industrial Revolution was approximately 2000 years before the present (BP). At this point the global lead production was about 10^5 tonnes per year. The concentration of lead in the Greenland ice core at this time was approximately 3×10^{-12} grams of lead per gram of ice.

SAQ 3.3

Yes, they do appear to be correlated, as the values rise and fall together. There is also a direct physical link between the two items, so it might be acceptable to use one as a proxy for the other.

SAQ 3.4

During an ice age, because the planet was colder and ice covered so much land, the treeline – our proxy for the Arctic definition – was much further south than today. This means that the area of the Arctic would have been much larger than at present.

SAQ 3.5

Measurement of the CO_2 contained in a trapped gas is a direct measurement, not a proxy. This means it is very accurate.

SAQ 3.6

1   In an ice age, when the temperature is low, the CO_2 is also low, typically 180 to 200 ppm. When the temperature is highest, in the interglacials, the CO_2 is also high, at about 280 ppm for the most recent four interglacials and slightly lower at 260 ppm for the earliest five interglacials.

2   The 2008 atmospheric CO_2 concentration is 383 ppm. This is about 100 ppm higher than what it was in the most recent four interglacials, and it is about 120 ppm higher than the earliest five interglacials in the EPICA Dome C record.

SAQ 3.7

Over the last 10 000 years the Earth's climate appears to have remained in a warm, stable state for longer than was normal in the preceding climate cycles. This has probably been important for humans in that they have been able to develop agriculture and other aspects of civilisation without the major disruption that would be caused by the major rapid cooling associated with ice ages.

SAQ 3.8

There are probably many positive and negative feedback processes associated with climate, but in the Arctic, changes in ice cover are a particularly good example of positive feedback, as is the role of methane. Reduction of ice cover changes the albedo so that more heat is absorbed, warming the water and reducing ice cover still further. As the permafrost melts it may release methane, a powerful greenhouse gas, potentially raising global temperature and causing further melting of permafrost and release of methane. Paradoxically, the possible effect of ice melt on the ocean currents could provide a form of negative feedback. If the warm current flowing north past north-west Europe was to cease, then this would produce a major cooling effect. Whether this would be enough to restrict further ice melt is an interesting question.

References and Further reading

Alley, R. B. (2000) *The Two Mile Time Machine*, Princeton, Princeton University Press.

Arctic Climate Impact Assessment (2005) ACIA Scientific Report, http://www.acia.uaf.edu/pages/scientific.html (Accessed December 2008).

Hong, S., Candelone, J-P., Patterson, C. C. and Boutron, C. F. (1994) 'Greenland ice evidence of hemispheric lead pollution two millennia ago by Greek and Roman civilizations', *Science*, vol. 265, no. 5180, pp. 1841–43.

Kunzig, R. and Broecker, W. S. (2008) *Fixing Climate: The Story of Climate Science – and How to Stop Global Warming*, London, Green Profile.

Lopez, B. (1986) *Arctic Dreams*, New York, Charles Scribner's Sons.

Macdonald, R. W., Harner, T. and Fyfe, J. (2005) 'Recent climate change in the Arctic and its impact on contaminant pathways and interpretation of temporal trend data', *Science of the Total Environment*, vol. 342, no. 1–3, pp. 5–86.

Ruddiman, W. F. (2005) 'How did humans first alter global climate?', *Scientific American*, March, pp. 26–53.

Serreze, M. C. and Stroeve, J. C. (2008) 'Standing on the brink', *Nature Reports Climate Change*, vol. 2, no. 11, pp. 142–43.

Turney, C. S. M. and Brown, H. (2007) 'Catastrophic early Holocene sea level rise, human migration and the Neolithic transition in Europe', *Quaternary Science Reviews*, vol. 26, no. 17–18, pp. 2036–41.

Wiig, O., Born, E. W. and Pederson, L. T. (2003) 'Movements of female polar bears (*Ursus maritimus*) in the East Greenland pack ice', *Polar Biology*, vol. 26, no. 8, pp. 509–16.

Part 4

Ways of knowing the Arctic

Matthew Kurtz

Introduction

1

As you approach the end of your journey in the Arctic, it is useful to recall your route. In Part 1: Imagining the Arctic, Joe Smith started you off by asking, 'What do you already know about this part of the planet, and how do you know it?' He then used popular material – maps, news stories, children's books and art – to show how people come to know something about a place that they may never have visited. Joe also turned his attention in a historical direction, asking how European explorers first became acquainted with the North American Arctic in centuries past. He did this by way of some primary source material, the journals that the explorers themselves had written, which can still be found in book form in a few libraries around Britain. Of course, these were not all that Joe used. He also consulted a number of secondary sources, that is, books and articles that other people had written later, using the same primary sources but giving them a new interpretation, creating a new angle on the place. This is one way to get to know the Arctic.

In Part 2: Time in context and Part 3: Following the flows, you learned about the natural history of the landscape on Svalbard, a group of islands north of Norway. You followed some questions like, How did those tree trunks come to be there when there are no trees around? And how did those hills come to get their shape? There the author, Mark Brandon, used fieldwork to generate his questions and contribute answers. He also used contemporary scientific models to explain the environmental phenomena he saw. One example was the diagram of continental drift in Figure 2.13. Another was Broecker's conveyor belt, shown in Figure 3.17. Both models are comparable to children's dolls and model aeroplanes or, for that matter, to the maps discussed in Part 1, in that these models are all scaled-down versions of reality. Scientific models, however, can be enormously complicated – like the global atmospheric circulation models used on supercomputers – and they are generally used to predict the outcome of a change or to discern an earlier condition of the environment in some ongoing process. Mark, for instance, used that mountain-building model to explain how the land mass of Svalbard would have been much closer to the equator many millions of years ago, which partly explains why tropical fossils can be found on an island in the high Arctic.

Before you move on to your next destination in this course – the Nile River in Africa – take a few moments to consider the sources of the knowledge you have gained in the earlier parts of Block 2.

Activity 4.1   Tracing the flows of environmental knowledge

Some of the authors that Joe Smith and Mark Brandon cite as sources for their material include Gerard Mercator (Section 2.1 in Part 1), Glenn Gould (Section 4), Peter Clegg (Section 4), Martin Frobisher (Section 5), Sheila Watt-Cloutier (Section 5.1); Alfred Wegener (Section 3 in Part 2); and Fridtjof Nansen (Section 3 in Part 3). Spend about 20 minutes looking over the relevant pages and answering the questions below. Jot down a short list of answers for each question.

1   Where did each of the people listed above come from?

2   Can you determine the country or place where each got their idea? If so, where? How did they then circulate their idea?

3   Which authors are clearly people who made their home in the Arctic?

Discussion

One of the people cited in Part 1: Imagining the Arctic was the architect Peter Clegg. He travelled to the Arctic and he wrote that, 'In the UK each one of us is …' (Box 1.6). So I surmised that Clegg was probably from the United Kingdom. He got his idea from 'some calculations' that he had made before he left on the expedition (it's difficult to be more specific here) and apparently from conversations with his collaborator, Antony Gormley. One of the sources in Part 3: Following the flow was Fridtjof Nansen, who was from Norway. He got his idea about drifting ice from news about the loss and the subsequent discovery of a ship on opposite sides of the Arctic Ocean. This text does not say how he circulated his idea – books, perhaps? And since it says only that he was from Norway, I could not tell whether Nansen had lived in the Arctic. After all, only the northern part of that country is north of the treeline (see Figure 1.11), and I do not think that a three-year expedition across the polar ice cap counts as making a home in the Arctic. So I looked up some information about Nansen on the internet. It seems that he lived in Oslo, in the southern part of Norway. Thus, Nansen did not make it to my list of authors for the third question.

Should I be surprised that, among all the people cited in Block 2 so far, only one was a person who actually lives in the Arctic? I am not sure. On the one hand, there are roughly four million people living in the region, almost as many as the entire population of Scotland (now at five million). It is not a small number of people to overlook. And if you wanted to learn about environmental change in the Arctic, then one obvious source would be the experts who live there. So maybe I should be surprised that we have not heard from many people in the Arctic so far.

On the other hand, I need to keep the aims of earlier parts of Block 2 in mind. In Part 1, Joe Smith was asking about popular perceptions of the Arctic in Britain. That does not naturally lead to large numbers of citations from people who live in the Arctic. In Parts 2 and 3, Mark Brandon was looking at broad-scale changes, across millions of years and around a big chunk of the planet. That, too, can quickly lead one away from local expertise. And there is another consideration to keep in mind too. Though people from the Arctic were quite influential behind the scenes of scientific discovery, very few historically played any widely visible role in environmental studies.

That history is starting to change. Local expertise is becoming more visible in environmental studies, and in this part of Block 2 you will learn how scientists at major metropolitan universities are learning from the *traditional ecological knowledge (TEK)* of Inuit people in the Arctic. TEK is the knowledge about the environment held by members of a largely native or indigenous community (and the elders especially, who are often accorded particular respect as the 'living libraries' in their community). TEK is informed by oral traditions and acquired over many years from observation and the practice of outdoor livelihood skills. Yet the use of TEK in scientific research has been controversial. Here you will explore reasons why it has been contentious, and how TEK might be (and is) used with scientific research. These are important and challenging issues, since debates about TEK will probably influence the way environmental science is conducted in the future, and because you will most likely encounter TEK again and again, in one form or another, as you continue with environmental studies.

At the moment (2008), the use of TEK in Arctic environmental studies is still in an experimental phase. This is because many Arctic scientists are not familiar with the context in which indigenous people continue to produce TEK, nor with the social research methods that they could use to learn from native people. In fact, most studies that use TEK currently take the form of illustration, as if to say 'the report you are about to read is a good example that shows how you too can use TEK in your research.' Through such studies, many scientists are gradually discovering what they can learn from traditional ecological knowledge, and you will see examples of its value in the following pages as well. But if (or when) you ever follow such an example, it will be important to understand how TEK is generated before you put it to use in your own work. That is my purpose in these pages: to sketch some of the context in which Inuit TEK was acquired in the recent past, so you can better appreciate the different nature of traditional ecological knowledge when you encounter it again in your studies.

Towards that end, I invite you to explore the complexity of what 'tradition' means in traditional ecological knowledge in the Arctic. Some environmental scientists stumble with that aspect of TEK, and I suspect that the problem has to do with the concept of 'tradition' in the English language. The word is usually used to refer to something that does not change much – like 'a family tradition' – and often it is set in contrast to modern life, in contrast to science and technology. That leads some people to think of a 'traditional culture' as backward, or even primitive. For Inuit cultures, that association is mistaken. Many people probably appreciate this fact based on documentaries they have seen about Inuit people, where modern technologies are often prominently featured. Yet when it comes to traditional ecological knowledge, a sense of some 'unchanging' tradition tends to creep back in. That sense of 'tradition' can create many false expectations about TEK.

I will come back to questions about what, exactly, is 'traditional' about Inuit TEK in the fourth section. The next two sections circle around this issue before I come back to it, head-on, at a later point. The roundabout progression will help you to think about traditions in a rather different way. It will take some work, because ideas about this one word – 'traditional' – are deeply ingrained in many of the concepts that many English-speaking people find available for thought.

The next section introduces you to Iñupiaq Eskimo communities in Arctic Alaska. It provides a little context about modern life in the Arctic. Then Section 3 will explore how many people learned about their environment in the North American Arctic. My purpose there is not to critique, nor to extol, Inuit practices of teaching and knowledge acquisition. Rather, it is to help you see why culture, language, and especially personal experience, are so important to the kind of knowledge that many Inuit people and others in the Arctic can contribute to scientific research. That will take you into the fourth section, where you will reconsider the issue of tradition. Many consider the 'traditional' part of Inuit TEK to be not just stories and customs passed down from ancestors, but also a long-standing tradition of experimentation and adaptation. One might ask how well TEK integrates with the methods of environmental science. There are different answers to that question. Some are very hopeful and positive, but others are more sceptical. I will touch on three distinct responses in the fifth and final section.

Arctic communities in Alaska today

2

I am a historical and economic geographer by training, and my research is about the geographies of economic development and the history of commercial tourism in the Arctic. For a number of years, my work has taken me to a community on the north-west Arctic coast of Alaska. There are no roads leading that far north. Villages are scattered on the coast and along major rivers. Travel is usually by plane, small boat, or snowmobile. Most people who live in this part of Alaska claim Iñupiaq Eskimo ancestry, but there are also many who do not.

Study note: language and identity

You may have noticed my use of the words 'Iñupiaq Eskimo' instead of 'Inuit' above. Let me explain. Of course, scholars in every field need to be careful in their language. Precision and clarity have always been key skills that students, teachers and researchers must practise in their writing. But many people are also concerned about the effects of unacceptable words. Language that is considered to be racist, sexist or homophobic is increasingly unacceptable, and in some contexts it is illegal. But it is also worth pausing a moment to consider how indigenous groups in the Arctic were named (and by whom), in order to better understand the strong passions and the long history of discrimination and exploitation that generated these concerns. Many people around the world now recognise that the words you use, because of their histories and their effects, sometimes require a challenging level of attention and care.

'Inuit' is an indigenous classification, a word of native origin, and many indigenous people in Arctic North America call themselves Inuit. The word generally includes the same people that others called Eskimo. But in Canada, that synonym is avoided. There it was derived from a French word, 'Esquimaux,' and it is thought to be a derogatory term invented by outsiders in scornful reference to the Inuit. This gets more complicated: Native people of Arctic Alaska, on the other hand, do occasionally call themselves 'Eskimos'. Since French was rarely used in Alaska, the word does not carry such unwelcome connotations there. But the indigenous people of northern Alaska also call themselves 'Iñupiaq' in their native language, and many use this as a more specific identification, one of three – Iñupiaq, Yupik, or Aleut – from different parts of Alaska (whose languages are similar but distinct). Like many in Alaska, I have chosen to use the two words together, 'Iñupiaq Eskimo', in order to be specific to the indigenous people of northern Alaska, while also accommodating those readers who may be more familiar with the broader classificatory term 'Eskimo'.

153

Jobs in Alaska's north-west Arctic can be relatively few and far between, in smaller villages especially. In April 2007, for example, the official unemployment rate in the region (at 11.9%) was almost twice the Alaska-wide average, and over 2.5 times the US average. On top of this, prices at local stores are considerably higher owing to the cost of air freight to bring goods to the Arctic. A study in 2008, for instance, showed that the weekly cost of groceries in the largest community in north-west Arctic Alaska was nearly twice as much as its weekly cost in Alaska's largest city, Anchorage (a major shipping hub on the south coast of the state). Accordingly, many people who live in northern Alaska – Iñupiaq as well as others from other parts of the world – put a lot of food on their table by fishing, hunting and gathering. According to one survey, members of a small community called Shungnak (population 248) harvested over 250 kg of wild food per person, on average, between January and December in 2002. Keep in mind that none of this food was sold for money; that gives you an idea how much less comes from the grocery store in this part of the Arctic. The composition of Shungnak's harvest is shown in Table 4.1.

Table 4.1 The harvest of wild food in Shungnak, Alaska, in 2002		
Type of wild food	Kilograms harvested (total) in Shungnak January to December 2002	Kilograms harvested per person (on average)
Fish	38256	154.3
Caribou	24886	100.3
Moose	2583	10.4
Birds and eggs	1206	4.9
Berries	1077	4.3
Other types	898	3.6

Source: Magdanz et al., 2004

SAQ 4.1   The daily use of wild foods

Use Table 4.1 to calculate your answers to the following questions.

1   How many kilograms of all types of wild food were harvested by each person (on average) in this Arctic community in 2002?

2   What percentage of all types of wild food, by weight, was fish in 2002?

3   On average, how many kilograms of wild food (all types) were harvested by each person in this community on a daily basis in 2002?

Now, if you live south of the Arctic, these statistics may conjure up the sorts of image that you often see in the media for Inuit people particularly: one or two individuals, warmly dressed, doing 'traditional' Inuit sorts of things like hunting. In newsprint and on TV, the next step is usually to claim that the Inuit have close and distinctive ties to the land. And because of these ties, it is assumed that environmental changes will have major impacts on all of them. Moreover, experts seem to agree that climate change is occurring most rapidly in the Arctic. So Inuit people, according to many writers, have become the 'first witnesses' of climate change on the planet.

There is a lot of evidence to support these claims. Among all that evidence, let me offer just two stories from a weekly newspaper in northern Alaska: *The Arctic Sounder*. What you see in Figure 4.1 is the headline story that appeared in that paper on 11 October 2007. The story was about the unexpected appearance of roughly 6000 female walrus and calves in September 2007 on Alaska's northern coast. Usually they are on pack ice on the Arctic Ocean in September, hundreds of miles north of Alaska's coastline. But during the summer of 2007, ocean ice had retreated at a record pace. The herd seemed healthy and the animals had plenty of fat. But local subsistence hunters noted that they had no food in their stomachs, and local residents were alarmed by their unusual presence and behaviour.

BEACHED BY CLIMATE CHANGE

Courtesy photo/V. Karve

Hordes of walrus haul out to the shores of Vankarem on the Chukchi Sea in the Russian Far East in a similar event to that noted on the North Slope, which has been linked to increased distance between the Siberian shore and Arctic pack ice.

Walrus crowd North Slope beaches

Surprised scientists cite global warming

TAMAR BEN-YOSEF
tbenyosef@alaskanewspapers.com

Thousands of walrus have shown up unexpectedly on North Slope coasts, surprising scientists who blame global warming and giving Alaska Native hunters an extra chance to harvest the hefty animals.

Biologists have spotted huge herds of Pacific walrus along some 300 miles of Chukchi Sea beaches between Barrow and Cape Lisburne in Northwest Alaska, said walrus biologist Tony Fischbach with the U.S. Geological Survey.

The unusual haul-out likely comes because the pack ice, where nearly all female walrus and calves usually spend summers, melted at a record pace this year, retreating to areas where walrus can't

See Page 9, **Walrus**

Figure 4.1 Six thousand walrus make the headlines in *The Arctic Sounder*, 11 October 2007

Another story was about the need to relocate an entire village on the Arctic coast. Changing weather has brought more severe storms across the sea, which causes faster rates of shoreline erosion. One village of about 350 people has suffered regular damage. Waves have started to reach the foundation of its school facilities. As a temporary measure, local officials funded the construction of a sea wall made of 'super sacks' filled with sand and gravel. It failed when a storm hit in September 2007, punching a 250-foot hole in these reinforcements. Yet the sea wall was only supposed to last until the village moved to higher ground, which it had planned to do years ago. The problem has been money. Some estimates have been over $300m to relocate the residents and their homes – modern houses, not the igloos that some readers might expect (see Figure 4.2) – and the government has balked at the cost. That has left the community's predicament to major media outlets as a regular story.

Figure 4.2 A September storm pounds an 800 foot-long wall of 'super sacks' after the temporary evacuation of an Arctic village, shown here in *The Arctic Sounder*, 20 September 2007

So stories in the local newspaper are underlining the impacts of climate change in northern Alaska. But is it wise to think of residents of the Arctic generally as the 'first witnesses' to climate change? No doubt the damage it can do (and is doing) is severe in the north. But is it any less severe for those who live on the coastal delta of the Ganges River in south Asia? The melting glaciers mentioned in Part 2 have already contributed to rising sea levels. If they continue to do so, millions who live a few feet above sea level in Bangladesh will be dislocated. Or consider the storm in December 2007 illustrated in Figure 2.20. It covered London with an inch of snow and shut down the city. My point is not that, for Iñupiaq or Inuit people in the Arctic, the dangers from climate change are relatively small. Rather, my point is that it may be a touch misleading to call them the 'first witnesses' of climate change, no matter how dramatic such stories look.

If you are on your toes, you may now want to say something about my missing the point. You might be thinking that the thing that makes Inuit people especially good candidates for the media's stories is their close ties to the land, ties which are at risk with climate change. My response is that I don't think that kind of story presents a rich picture of Inuit life in the Arctic. But then, how could you learn more about life in this part of the Arctic, short of actually spending time there? What 'ways of knowing the Arctic' are accessible to you as an Open University student? One possibility is to read an Arctic newspaper regularly, provided one is available in a language you can understand. I read *The Arctic Sounder* for a year, for instance, before I started any fieldwork in Arctic Alaska, and I continue to read it regularly. Moreover, reading the local newspaper regularly is a common thing to do if your research might be taking you to another part of the world. Of course, newspapers don't tell you everything. They miss all sorts of details, big and small. But if you want to learn more about a distant community, if you want a richer picture of what it is like to live there, then its local newspaper might help. It often provides an abundance of qualitative evidence about everyday life in a place.

Study note: quantitative v. qualitative evidence

Quantitative evidence is concerned with the quantity, measure or proportion of things. Examples include the population of an Arctic community, their average annual income, or the percentage who self-identify as Iñupiaq. Quantitative evidence was used in Table 4.1, for instance, to show how much food the people of Shungnak put on their tables by harvesting it themselves, rather than going to a store. A common way in which social scientists collect quantitative data is through a limited-answer survey, which involves asking lots of people the same short questions. Quantitative evidence is usually presented in the form of numbers, tables or graphs. This kind of evidence would probably be used if you want to contribute to the thinking of mainstream policy makers, business analysts or biologists.

Qualitative evidence is concerned with the quality or character of things. Examples include stories about what people do for fun in an Arctic village, or a description of their feelings, or a picture of what those activities look like. In Figure 4.2, for instance, the aerial photo offered qualitative evidence about the character of modern life in an Arctic community. Ways to collect qualitative data include interviews, attitude surveys, participant observation and photography, as well as drawing material from the arts, biographies and news stories. Such data is usually presented in the form of words or images. This form of evidence would probably be used if you want to understand how, for instance, everyday life is experienced in an Arctic community.

What can the local newspaper, *The Arctic Sounder*, tell you about life in this part of the Arctic? What evidence does it provide about the everyday experience of residents? Well, it can show other aspects of life in this place, aspects that make one-dimensional associations between environmental

Figure 4.3 A high school basketball match in Barrow, Alaska. Photo from *The Arctic Sounder*, 8 March 2007

change and Iñupiaq people more difficult to sustain. One such aspect is fun. There are probably things you can imagine yourself doing for fun in the Arctic: riding a snowmobile may come to mind. But would it surprise you to learn that basketball is among the most popular sports in Arctic Alaska (Figure 4.3)? If you read the paper, you will find that many travel long distances to attend basketball games in one another's school facilities.

Paid employment is another aspect of life that you would learn about in the local newspaper. Residents of north-west Arctic Alaska live near one of the world's largest zinc mines. A regional Native corporation owns part of the mine, and roughly 50% of the 500 employees at the facility are people who claim Iñupiaq ancestry from the region. Their jobs at the mine may help support a household in one of the Arctic villages, including buying and maintaining the snowmobiles that their family needs for transportation and hunting. On top of that, the mine indirectly supports other jobs throughout the region. But it also comes with risks of pollution, which could contaminate the fish and animals that are harvested around the area. Such risks and benefits are often the subject of articles and images in *The Arctic Sounder*.

All of this is to say that to imagine Inuit people solely as the first witnesses of climate change may paint a one-dimensional picture, and there are things you can do – like reading a local newspaper – to add more breadth to what you know about the Arctic. Its residents can certainly put a human face on climate change for major media outlets, and this is very valuable. But it is not the only thing that the diverse residents of the Arctic can teach a student of environmental studies: as one climate-change geographer in Canada points out, 'there are many other issues besides climate change that concern Inuit' (Fox, 2002, p. 45). Indeed, you might not be able to build a rich and meaningful analysis of what is going on if the only thing you hoped to learn, when talking with a long-time resident of the North, was simply something about their environment.

Activity 4.2   Using qualitative and quantitative evidence

In this section I have used both quantitative and qualitative evidence to argue that climate change, while critically important, is not the only subject of interest in the region. Now consider how important money is in this part of the world. Money and the resources it can acquire are very important in Arctic Alaska, but perhaps not overwhelmingly so. Use 30 minutes to consider the two questions below. Write up your thoughts in 150–200 words.

1 What *quantitative* evidence offered in Section 2 might support the claim that money is very important (but perhaps not overwhelmingly so) in Arctic Alaska?

2 What *qualitative* evidence in Section 2 might support this same claim?

Discussion

To my surprise, I thought the quantitative evidence above does support the claim that money is not overwhelmingly important in Arctic Alaska. I found myself paying close attention to the figures for the harvest of wild foods. It all involved the harvest and distribution of food without any money changing hands. I was especially struck by the weight of berries picked by a person, on average, in this Arctic community. I pick wild berries occasionally, but to pick 4 kg of them every summer would take some time (and, mind you, that's the average harvest per person, so some pick much more)! On the other hand, the limited qualitative evidence suggested that money was nonetheless very important in this part of Alaska. Here, I found the photo of the basketball game striking. A lot of money was necessary to create the moment when that picture was taken – funds for the facility, money to heat the gymnasium in March, money to outfit the players, money to pay for the fuel that the audience used to get there. So from that visual (qualitative) evidence, I surmised that money plays quite an important role in Arctic Alaska. Such games would be difficult without the imported resources that money had brought to the area. Then there was some mixed evidence above, as in the story about village relocation. Money was at issue, but was it the qualitative or quantitative evidence that convinced me? It was both, but more the first, I think, because the description of the situation (the story, or the qualitative evidence) was what carried me, whereas the estimate of the cost, over $300 million (that was the quantitative data presented), could have been described in qualitative terms as simply 'a large amount of money' to almost as much effect.

Summary of Section 2

Section 2 introduced you to a few predominantly Iñupiaq Eskimo communities in Arctic Alaska. It provided some background about the character of modern life in this part of the Arctic, and it argued that issues of climate change, while critically important, are not the only matters of concern to its residents. In addition to learning about the context of life in the Arctic, you distinguished between quantitative and qualitative forms of evidence in the social sciences, and you learned of the potential value of local newspapers for adding breadth to your knowledge of a distant region or place in the world.

3

Teaching styles in the recent past

In the last section I introduced you to some communities in Arctic Alaska, places where scientists are carrying out a considerable amount of environmental research into wildlife, pollutants and climate change. Since the 1990s a growing portion of this research has involved the use of traditional ecological knowledge or TEK. But that development has been slow. One environmental scientist who works with TEK in Alaska explains, in part, why this is the case:

> Many wildlife managers and researchers are unfamiliar with social science methods and are not prepared to attempt to use these methods to gain access to information that otherwise remains out of reach. They may also be uncomfortable in cross-cultural interactions.

(Huntington, 2000)

Even so, more and more environmental scientists are now trying methods from the social sciences in order to make use of TEK in their research. As they do so, they are learning about different interview techniques, focus groups, participant observation and other data collection techniques that researchers can learn more about in the social sciences. As you pursue your studies further, it is quite likely that you will read of numerous examples where TEK was used, in one form or another, for some environmental research.

But working with TEK also requires a major shift in the way some scientists think about what counts as knowledge. TEK and scientific knowledge are not entirely alike, so attention and care must be given to the ways in which TEK is acquired and communicated if it is to be applied to environmental research. In this section you will learn about some of the ways in which an older generation of Inuit people learned about their environment and how TEK was generated.

There are two points that I ask you to keep in mind along the way. First, there is a lot of diversity in TEK. The point is probably not surprising if you compare TEK with the sciences in the industrialised world. The methods and perspectives that Joe Smith used as a social scientist in Part 1, for instance, were considerably different from those that Mark Brandon used as a natural scientist in Part 2, so 'western' knowledge is not all alike. The same holds true for traditional ecological knowledge. Not only is Inuit TEK in Arctic North America rather different from Saami TEK in northern Europe, but within Inuit TEK as well, the diversity of observations, experiences and opinions tends to be valued more than consensus when it comes to knowledge about the environment.

Second, my purpose is not to critique, or to extol, the practices of teaching and knowing among Inuit traditional knowledge bearers. My intention is not to pass any such judgements. Rather, what I offer in this section serves as a means to an end. It is designed to help you better understand what TEK might have to offer an environmental scientist, and why the word 'traditional' can be misleading in that regard. To that end, you will explore the role of *socialisation* and teaching styles in the formation of Inuit TEK in the recent past.

What is 'socialisation' about? It is a term that sociologists use for those processes of social interaction through which a person learns to be a member of a culture, group, or institution. Through socialisation people learn the effects and effective limits of different sorts of behaviour. In youth it helps to shape one's personality, values and patterns of reasoning. While it varies from person to person with the influence of different forces (ethnicity, gender, class, locale, etc.), socialisation is the process through which a culture or institution reproduces itself.

Activity 4.3   Socialisation at The Open University

You might think that little socialisation takes place among Open University (OU) students, but the institution could not work without it. Through it, you learn about:

1 your own role and what is expected of you as a student

2 the roles of different staff members (administration, IT, tutors, etc.)

3 forms of communication (text books, email, etc.) that are used at different times

4 what kinds of question you can ask, and what is expected in your answers.

Use 20 minutes to consider one or two aspects (above) of your own socialisation into OU culture. Write a 100-word paragraph describing in greater detail how it worked.

Discussion

Socialisation is not always pleasant (though I hope your experience with the OU has been enjoyable) because, when you are new to an institution, you sometimes learn what others consider to be a 'mistake' only after you have done it. But the process is not just negative. It also takes place through quiet celebrations that follow after a new person does something that more experienced members consider proper or correct.

One example of socialisation is the way very young people are taught how they should ask questions, and when it is appropriate to do so. Through socialisation, Inuit children in times past often learned that it was out of place for them to ask questions. According to elders like Emile Imaruittuq, 'in Inuit tradition, we were not to ask when we were curious' (Figure 4.4). Adults asked the questions, and children were taught to watch and listen carefully to discover answers to a problem. Being able to learn by watching and listening was considered 'a great tool for life, as it teaches you more than just random questioning' (Imaruittuq, in Kunuk, 2001).

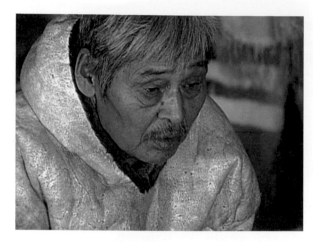

Figure 4.4 'In Inuit tradition, we were not to ask when we were curious,' says Emile Imaruittuq (pictured)

Other elders report that, in camps, when they were children they were trained to be attentive weather observers. They were woken early and directed outside to relate the wind and sky conditions. Called *anijaaq*, the daily assignment honed their observation skills and socialised young people into sharing knowledge about the weather. One Inuit elder, Paul Qulitalik, also reports that

> When we [boys] got old enough, our fathers woke us up at dawn to go hunting, even in the coldest conditions. We were also given outside chores during the coldest times of the year [Figure 4.5]. Our parents were very aware of what needed to be done. We were taught certain things according to our age and maturity. I know from experience that it is a very effective way to teach a child new skills.

(Qulitalik, in Kunuk, 2001)

Figure 4.5 Young boys were 'given outside chores during the coldest times of the year', says Paul Qulitalik (pictured)

Along with socialisation, language is another key component in the generation of different forms of knowledge. Over the last three decades, many social scientists have argued that differences in language and meaning structure one's perception. Consider English words for food, for instance, which tend to depersonalise the animal on the plate. One might speak of having 'lamb' or 'fish' or 'chicken' for dinner; to talk of having a lamb, a fish or a chicken for dinner is not as common. If language helps to shape how one sees things, Inuit leaders have been drawing on that point to encourage researchers and conservation specialists to pay closer attention to their own indigenous languages. Speaking with scientists as a former president of the Inuit Circumpolar Conference, Mary Simon has pointed out that:

> Our [Inuit] languages are rich in ecological concepts and descriptions of the environment. If true partnerships are sought, and a genuine desire to better understand our 'non-western' thought processes exists, then it will be necessary to also work with our languages. We have already demonstrated our willingness to work with yours.

(Simon, 1995)

Now consider the word 'teach'. If you think that the Inuit have dozens of words for what I might just call 'snow', then English has no shortage of synonyms for the verb 'to teach' (see Figure 4.6).

11   VERBS **teach, instruct,** give instruction, give lessons in, **educate, school; edify, enlighten,** civilize, illumine; **direct, guide;**

Figure 4.6   Some synonyms for the word 'teach' in the author's copy of *Roget's Thesaurus*

But Inuit dialects make an interesting distinction between two general styles of teaching, with two words: *ilisayuq* and *isummaksaiyuq*. Both mean 'to teach', but *ilisayuq* refers to the formal educational style that teachers from industrialised parts of North America often used in the past in the Arctic. The root word, *ilit-*, means 'to learn (it)' and *ilisayuq* means to lecture, to practise correct answers by drill, to invite students to memorise, to cause learning. In contrast, the root word for *isummaksaiyuq* is *isuma*, which translates roughly as thought or reason. One common translation of *isummaksaiyuq* then is 'to cause thought'. *Isummaksaiyuq* is to encourage a student to observe, to experiment, to give careful thought to the problem or material at hand. Both words mean 'to teach', but in Inuit languages it seems to have been useful (at least in times past) to distinguish between helping someone become educated or learned (*ilisayuq*) on the one hand, and helping them become observant and thoughtful (*isummaksaiyuq*) on the other.

The distinction is important because, as a teaching style, *isummaksaiyuq* may have fashioned the acquisition of TEK some years ago among many Inuit, more than a few of whom are now working with environmental scientists as traditional knowledge bearers. Three examples help to illustrate the point about this style of teaching, and similar examples were observed across Arctic North America during the years when many contemporary Inuit elders and other knowledge bearers would have been old enough themselves to be new parents.

3.1 Three examples of *isummaksaiyuq*

1 Regarding navigation

Up to the 1980s, anthropologists were finding that many Inuit adults would question and test children while travelling. In a boat or at rest with snowmobiles, someone might ask them 'Which way is town from here?' or 'Have you been here before?' Along the many bends in a river, or on a stretch of tundra, in a landscape that can look very different from one season to the next, children were often asked to puzzle out where they were based on what they had seen on the journey. These questions were meant to cause thought: *isummaksaiyuq*. If the young person could not figure out an answer on the spot, the grown-ups would be amused and the youth would be encouraged to pay closer attention on their travels.

2 Regarding danger

So long as lives were not at risk, parents often chose not to prevent their children from heading into dangerous situations. This sits in some contrast to a risk-averse, 'health and safety' culture that many claim to be characteristic of child rearing in Britain. But life in the Arctic can be quite precarious: the weather can suddenly change, the ice can break underneath you, and you can quickly get lost. Instead of setting rules or forbidding certain activities ('Don't play with fire' or 'You cannot go that far away'), many Inuit parents simply warned children about the likely consequences ('If you play with fire, you will get burned') and then let the environment teach its own lessons. This was often possible in a camp or a smaller community, since family and close neighbours could watch out for the kids while acting uninterested, so as to give the children a sense of independence. Under such conditions, young people had considerable freedom to experiment, to test their choices, to decide themselves what worked best in a dangerous environment: *isummaksaiyuq*. If they made a mistake, an adult would only need to remind them about it once in a while to get them to think: 'Do you remember?'

3 Regarding behaviour

Freedom to test their environment is one thing, but how could children learn to behave among adults without stern lectures and reprimands? To answer this question, one anthropologist spent six months in the 1970s in an Inuit camp on Baffin Island (Briggs, 1998). She found that people in the camp guided one three-year-old girl's behaviour by playfully asking her questions – like 'How am I related to you?' – and letting her solve them. One frequent question was a treacherous one for the girl: 'Are you a baby?' As her relatives questioned and teased her, they helped her learn that *being* a baby had consequences, some good (adorable, helpless baby) and some bad (horrid, thoughtless baby). And by asking her to think about her behaviour in these terms, they helped her see that she could choose to act like a baby. But getting out of that act was difficult: if she was thoughtless and uncontrolled, she was (to put it in abstract terms) by definition a baby. 'Are you a baby? No?' End of conversation. But when the little girl began to respond to that question by saying 'yes' and *pretending* to be a baby (she deliberately mispronounced some words in a baby-like way), her response was encouraged. To the delight of her relatives, the little girl was growing up. She could pretend to be an adorable, helpless baby, but that meant she was being more thoughtful and controlling her behaviour and that, ironically, she was therefore no longer a baby. By presenting her with a problem she had to solve, her family and friends had encouraged the girl to experiment with her responses, to observe the consequences as adults pleasurably played them out, and to give careful thought to her own dilemma of babyhood: *isummaksaiyuq*.

In each of these examples, the environment or the adults (rather than the children) posed the problems. It was up to a young person to offer an answer, and it seems that lectures and rules were not so common. Again, this is not to commend or critique this teaching style. My purpose is only to sketch some of the context in which TEK was acquired by many (not all) who are now elders in the Arctic.

SAQ 4.2   Are you in *isummaksaiyuq* school now?

Respond to each of the following questions with a short answer.

1   What is a rough translation of the Inuit word *isummaksaiyuq*?

2   Has my teaching style over the last couple of pages used *isummaksaiyuq* or *ilisayuq*?

3   Which style does your U116 tutor seem to favour, *isummaksaiyuq* or *ilisayuq*?

4   How is *socialisation* defined in the social sciences?

5   Is *isummaksaiyuq* a form of socialisation?

As many writers point out, Inuit have lived in a world where little was predictable and little stayed the same for very long. The caribou upon which an Inuit village relied for sustenance, for instance, could quickly change their migration routes, no longer taking them anywhere near that community. Change and adaptation was key, and few assumed that things could not or would not change. This teaching style, *isummaksaiyuq*, may have helped to socialise Inuit elders into a frame of reference where few people took things for granted, where they instead looked for transformations, for the changing qualities of things: the weather, a growing toddler, ice, or a travel route.

It is more than just a tendency to be flexible and open to the sight of change, to be vigilant and observant, to refuse to jump to permanent conclusions.

A sceptical approach to the fixity of things also works through the way many in the Arctic are ready and willing to remake things, to be adaptive and resourceful. A tent was not necessarily just a tent, for instance. It could be torn down, rebuilt as a sled, and then rebuilt later as a tent again. Everything had within it the potential to be used in a different way. With ingenuity, each thing could become something else. A saw blade could be remade as a knife. Or a baby, when ready, could be encouraged to become a little girl, one who could also pretend to be a baby again, just for the fun of it. And that ingenuity, in part, may have been born out of a teaching style that encouraged thoughtful problem solving and experimentation. Jaypetee Arnakak (2000, p. 11) has suggested something similar: 'There is no single defining factor of being Inuit, but this comes close. Inuit culture is [about] *qanuqtuurunnaaniq*, or the concept of being resourceful to solve problems.'

It is also important to note that the three examples above each come from the 1970s and 1980s. That was when most of the Inuit people who are now the more experienced traditional knowledge bearers were old enough to be new parents themselves. With all the changes in recent decades, you may want to be cautious before you make any sweeping conclusions without further evidence, either that *isummaksaiyuq* (as I have described it) is the primary and traditional 'Inuit style' to teach, or that these three examples are still widely applicable in communities in northern North America. It is likely that the dynamics of education in this part of the Arctic have changed, both at home and in the school systems. One recent development, for instance, is that some elders like Emile Imaruittuq are now encouraging young people to ask them questions. Another development is that a good number of teenagers in Arctic North America are becoming involved in scientific research, collecting data with scientists who work at universities elsewhere (see Box 4.1). This may well change the nature of TEK over time.

> ### Box 4.1   A contemporary environmental education in the Arctic
>
>
>
> **Figure 4.7 AliceAnne Fournier and Uinniq Ahgeak suit up to collect eelgrass samples near Cold Bay, Alaska**

For four Barrow teens, a summer spent helping biologists study the threatened Steller's eider has garnered them Alaska's 'Spirit of Youth' award. AliceAnne Fournier, Uinniq Ahgeak, Sean Gueco and Siggy Patterson spent last summer walking between six to eight miles a day around Barrow collecting data on the eider birds, such as where they nest, breeding habits and learning about the birds' predators, said project manager Neesha Wendling, a Fish and Wildlife biologist from Fairbanks.

Wendling leads the project that hires four Barrow students and a teacher every year to do scientific research work, such as conducting eelgrass research with University of Alaska Fairbanks professor Peter McRoy. The project has grown since it first started in 1999.

The four youths shared the distinction of being finalists in the science and environment division with four girls in Kotzebue who conducted a three-year science project. Ariana Walker, Jasmine Kirk, Anna Lincoln and Tiffany Creed tested natural oils extracted from plants around Kotzebue for their uses in fighting bacteria.

Walker, Kirk, Lincoln and Creed spent countless hours at the Maniilaq Health Center lab testing 23 essential oils taken from items such leedum, or tundra tea. The direction of their testing was dictated largely by stories told to them by Elders, many of them in the local senior center. The girls discovered leedum fought the spread of staph or E. coli at twice the rate of the best antibiotic.

(Adapted from Ipsen, 2007)

Summary of Section 3

This section took you into the world of teaching and learning that was probably familiar to many of today's Inuit traditional knowledge bearers when they were young. That background, drawn from everyday practices in Arctic North America in the 1970s and 1980s, was important because it helps us to understand how contemporary Inuit TEK was acquired, and what TEK might now have to offer environmental researchers from the industrialised world. Towards that end, you learned that the process of socialisation was central to many Inuit 'ways of knowing the Arctic'. They were based on forms of learning where adults usually asked the questions, and where individual experimentation, ingenuity and adaptation were highly encouraged among young people.

4   Tradition and *Inuit Qaujimajatuqangit*

If you continue in environmental studies, it is likely that you will encounter TEK again, and the previous section may help you better understand how contemporary Inuit TEK has often been generated and acquired by those who share it. Yet that word 'traditional' in traditional ecological knowledge can be misleading. It can paint a picture of opposites, of 'traditional knowledge' that sits in stark contrast to modern science. Indeed, for scientists who are new to the topic, it often prompts a picture of old stories and legends. That is what many researchers think TEK can offer science: they often consider it as another source of historical evidence, as data that can be recovered from stories and songs. It is true that this kind of data recovery is possible. Writers have found that elders in Nunavut knew old stories about Frobisher from the 1570s, and that historical documents corroborated information that Inuit informants had recently recalled about changing caribou populations in the middle of the twentieth century. And it is all too easy to concentrate on these sorts of potential contribution in the belief that they are what 'traditional' knowledge is all about.

The important point, however, is that many people in the Arctic think that *adaptation* is the central characteristic of Inuit culture, rather than its legends or stories. That perspective looks more to its traditions of vigilant observation, experimentation and change; its customs of solving problems resourcefully with whatever was at hand, when possible; and its tradition of transforming things and people – the bones of an animal which now becomes a sculpture, a modified engine that creates a better snowmobile, or the culture itself in rapidly changing times.

Box 4.2   Stray muskox calls forth different rules of tradition

Figure 4.8 Muskox in northern Alaska

'Tradition' is a slippery concept, but its interpretation can have very substantial consequences. Here is one example of the real difference that this language of 'tradition' can make.

In the 1980s, a muskox wandered alone far from its normal habitat, approaching a Yupik Eskimo village in south-west Alaska. Two boys asked the community elders whether they should shoot it. The elders encouraged them to do so. As with many Inuit around the Arctic, they shared an understanding that any animal that offered itself to a hunter should be taken. Not to do so was thought to disrespect the animal, which was a significant offence. The boys shot the muskox and distributed the meat around the village in the customary ways.

The two boys were then arrested by police, and subsequently fined for shooting a muskox out of season. State lawyers argued that muskox were not a traditional source of game for the community. They had not been hunted there before, so the defence – that the boys had followed Yupik traditions – did not hold. According to prosecutors and conservation officials, the boys had simply broken a state law designed to maintain the muskox population.

'Tradition' is usually understood as the practices that remain unchanged. But here it is not entirely clear which practice should be considered traditional. Tradition could be the sorts of animal that a community customarily harvests at a certain time of year. That was the view of the legal system. Or it could be the way that local decisions are made about harvesting wildlife in a changing world. That was the view of the elders.

To get a better handle on the tricky issue of 'tradition' in TEK, you may want to distinguish between *storied TEK* and *skilled TEK*. Storied knowledge is the TEK that is learned through the repetition of stated information, through *ilisayuq*, through the form and content of stories that each generation receives and passes along to the next like a baton. It takes shape in stories, songs and legends, and it is understood to be knowledge acquired prior to its application or expression in real life. Since most people assume that this kind of knowledge can be learned almost anywhere (a classroom or courtroom might work), this is the kind of knowledge that scientists and lawyers often look for: 'traditional knowledge' in the form of stories about the distant past that mention a sequence of hard winters, for instance, or the harvest of muskox in a particular area.

Skilled traditional knowledge, on the other hand, cannot be displaced from the person who holds it. For this sort of knowledge, experience is everything. Take weather, for example. In the Arctic, weather prediction skills are not handed down to a student through a set of explanations and models like those that Mark Brandon offered in Part 3. Rather, such skills grow through the experience of living in a place, perhaps starting when a child is sent outside every morning to observe the weather (*anijaaq*) and is personally queried about it (*isummaksaiyuq*). Such tacit knowledge cannot be taught in classrooms. It is inseparable from living on the land because it is generated from the relationships that knowledge bearers slowly forge with their environment. It is 'traditional' knowledge, not because it is unchanging, but because each person develops their own skilled knowledge in the context of similar activities with older generations of family and friends.

When working with Inuit TEK, new scientists can underestimate the significance of personal experience in the kind of knowledge they may be offered. What many contemporary elders often consider most valuable are the details they can offer (e.g. 'I have never seen a muskox around the village before. But I saw two over there seven years ago'). They usually focus on specifics and details. Indeed, many are sceptical of scientists' claim to some general expertise (after all, how can a porcupine biologist from a city hundreds of miles away know all about the local porcupines, too?) Traditional knowledge bearers tend to seek out variations in each other's experience, and flatly contradictory reports are often accepted without comment. Most think such diversity in experience and understanding should be expected in an environment where everything changes, and where children had been encouraged to make their own observations and draw their own conclusions. On the other hand, Inuit elders and traditional knowledge bearers often view general statements (e.g. 'the normal habitat for muskox is 40 miles from that village') as vague, and sometimes even dangerous. This runs against the inclinations of most scientists, who usually like to resolve discrepancies and to synthesise many observations and details into a general statement.

SAQ 4.3   Reviewing what's 'traditional' about Inuit TEK

Respond to each of the following questions with a short answer.

1   What word summarises what many people in the Arctic believe to be the central characteristic of Inuit culture?
2   Why is the word 'traditional' in traditional ecological knowledge (TEK) problematic?
3   In what sense is *storied* TEK traditional?
4   In what sense is *skilled* TEK traditional?
5   A true statement about the prevailing winds (i.e. the general tendency of direction for the winds) in an Arctic location would be considered desirable and useful in whose tradition: in that of Inuit elders, in the tradition of scientists, or in that of both?

I have been saying that this word 'tradition' creates some false expectations in regard to TEK, that it creates a number of problems and likely misunderstandings in regard to the changing nature of TEK. So why don't people just get rid of the troublesome word and call that knowledge something else?

That is what people in the eastern Arctic of Canada have started to do. In a conference on traditional knowledge in 1998, Inuit elders started writing out some principles that they called **Inuit Qaujimajatuqangit**. It is usually abbreviated as *IQ* and it translates roughly as 'long-standing Inuit ways of knowing'. As you may know, *IQ* also stands for 'intelligence quotient' in English, which is thought to be a measure of how smart somebody is (so there was humour in renaming Inuit TEK as '*IQ*'). The participants believed that TEK was too narrowly defined and thus too often misunderstood. It had led many outside researchers to ask for ancient, unchanging knowledge. Moreover, the elders were disturbed that their knowledge had often been broken down into separate components. They had been asked to share their knowledge (TEK) about caribou, and then about wolves, as if each species was unrelated to the other. It seemed to discourage scientists from asking about their understanding of the ecological relationship between animals.

Inuit Qaujimajatuqangit is, accordingly, much broader in its focus. In contrast to traditional ecological knowledge or TEK, *IQ* was put forward as wisdom that included Inuit perspectives on relationships between living creatures. *IQ* referred to 'all aspects of traditional Inuit culture, including values, world-view, language, life skills, perceptions and expectations'. Elders wanted it to be understood as a philosophy, as 'a living technology' that draws on present-day thinking as well as that of the past. Some of the core guidelines of *IQ* stress the importance of:

1 respecting differences, especially when seeking consensus (*aajiiqatigiingniq*)

2 environmental stewardship, treating nature holistically (*avatimik kamattiarniq*)

3 treating all wildlife respectfully (*ikpigusuttiarniq nirjutilimaanik*)

4 serving, using one's power to serve others (*pijitsirniq*)

5 skills and knowledge acquisition through continual practice (*pilimmaksarniq*)

6 problem solving, creative improvisation (*qanuqtuurunnarniq*)

7 respecting the in-depth knowledge and experience of others (*qaujimanilik*)

8 avoiding unnecessary harm to animals (*sirliqsaaqtittittailiniq*)

9 avoiding waste in harvest (*surattittailimaniq*).

Activity 4.4   Measuring your own *Inuit Qaujimajatuqangit*

Take about 20 minutes to consider all nine guidelines above. They are currently listed in alphabetical order by the original Inuktitut word (in parentheses) that describes each guideline. Make a new list that shows how you would rank these guidelines in terms of their importance to you. You don't need to remember those Inuktitut words, but write a few comments about why you chose to put one or two of the guidelines at the bottom of your list.

Discussion

When I did this exercise, my first inclination was to tick all nine guidelines and leave them unranked. They struck me as universal, professed most everywhere in principle. Why would I disagree with any of them? But when I thought about my actual daily practices, some priorities took shape. As a social scientist, I thought (7), (4) and (1) probably go to the top on an everyday basis. (8), (6) and (5) landed in the middle as background fundamentals. Having grown up on a farm, they are simply what I have always done. I put (9) at the bottom. I really do not like to waste things (it is related to my 'avoid unnecessary harm' ethic), but the idea of a 'harvest' just does not resonate, since my partner and I shop for most of what we eat and use.

If the nine guidelines above struck you as fairly universal or cross-cultural in principle, then it is worth pausing with a couple of those guidelines in more detail. Consider (3), *ikpigusuttiarniq nirjutilimaanik*. Again, this was translated to mean, 'treating all wildlife with respect'. For many people in the industrialised world, to treat an animal with respect would mean not killing it, but what counts as respect can look different from another point of view. For many Inuit, the recipients of that respect – animals – are sentient beings, much like humans. From bears to beluga whales, from foxes to fish, gulls and geese, animals are understood to be feeling, thinking creatures that are usually more aware and sensitive to the world around them than their human counterparts. They are not seen as victims of circumstance. Instead, animals are considered to be willing and participating members of an ecological community who deliberately choose to return in large numbers if they and their habitat are treated well. To hunt geese properly and successfully thus requires a relationship of respect between the family of humans and the society of geese, who are thought to be aware how their kin are treated when hunted and eaten. Demonstrations of prowess, waste, carelessness or malice are considered to have no place when they are taken for subsistence.

According to that third guideline (*ikpigusuttiarniq nirjutilimaanik*), animals need to be approached and hunted with the right attitude. You have already encountered this issue in the story about the muskox, which was shot out of respect after it was seen to offer itself to the young hunters. A polar bear hunt on Baffin Island illustrates this particular guideline in better detail. In this case, respect went beyond adversarial esteem, involving a serious, solemn attitude and respect for its wishes when a polar bear had to be hunted.

Box 4.3   How one polar bear wanted to be approached

… while travelling through a small valley, the hunter saw the opening of a den about 400 m ahead and 150 m above our position. A bear emerged and immediately scented, then saw, the dogs and us. Surprisingly, the bear did not re-enter the den nor move away. Instead, it simply sat in front of the den entrance and looked at us.

Given the fact that the food situation in the village was serious and that we were in a position to take a substantial amount of meat, I expected that we would immediately begin an approach. However, the hunter did no such thing. Rather, he unpacked a telescope and began to study the bear. This continued for nearly three hours, the bear aware of us and we, but not the dogs, watching it. The hunter repeatedly remarked that he had never seen a bear acting as this one did, that he did not understand the bear and that I should be patient.

When he decided to approach the bear, I was told to follow with one dog. The hunter continued his approach until he was perhaps 25 m directly below the bear, and only then did he aim and shoot, killing it with that shot. The evening of our return, he recounted the details of the hunt. He repeatedly noted the odd behaviour of the bear and how he had become convinced that the successful conclusion of this hunt would turn on discerning how the animal wanted to be approached.

(Adapted from Wenzel, 2004)

If that third principle entails respect for the wishes of a wild animal, such respect will look very different depending on the way different people understand those wishes. That is to say, this guideline may not be as universal as it looks.

Or consider (2) in that list of guidelines above, *avatimik kamattiarniq*. It translates as environmental stewardship and 'treating nature holistically'. *Stewardship* is the careful and responsible management of something that has been entrusted to one's care. Few wildlife biologists are likely to disagree with the principle but again, a lot depends on how nature is understood, the weight of quantitative and qualitative information in that understanding, and what, exactly, is in need of stewardship. The example in Box 4.4 serves to illustrate this problem through a contentious wildlife management strategy. The argument turns on how a population of wild mountain sheep (see Figure 4.9) should be kept under control, with conflicting views between the indigenous people around Kluane Lake and government biologists in the Yukon Territory of Canada over the use of a quota system, which would have allowed only a limited number (or quota) of these Dall sheep to be shot every year in the region.

Box 4.4   Stewardship of Dall sheep in the Yukon

To manage a population of Dall sheep in the southwest Yukon, the Fish and Wildlife Management Board asked indigenous Kluane people, including elders and hunters, to recall the numbers of sheep they had seen over the years, as well as when and where these sightings had occurred. A series of maps was prepared from their accounts. This meant they had fully considered the traditional knowledge of the community.

But in discussions about regulating sheep hunting, members of the Kluane community expressed concern over the current practice of restricting hunters to shooting only full curl rams (these are fully mature rams eight years old or older). They argued that these animals are especially important to the overall sheep population because of their role as teachers; it is from these mature rams that younger rams learn proper mating behaviour as well as more general survival strategies. Thus, killing too many full curl rams has an impact on the population far in excess of the number of animals killed by hunters. One person likened it to killing off all the elders in their community.

As far as many members of the Kluane community were concerned, understanding the sheep's social structure and how the animals behave is every bit as important to them as the numbers sought by biologists. They had raised their concerns hoping to switch from a full curl rule to a quota system as a means to limit the sheep kill in the area. Both methods effectively limit the number of animals that can be killed, but a quota system would spread the kill more evenly over the entire sheep population, rather than focusing it on a particular age group.

The scientists and resource managers present at the meetings neither dismissed nor refuted this argument. They simply ignored it (since the argument would be difficult to prove scientifically) and asserted that there was simply no need for a quota because the full curl rule effectively limited the number of sheep taken. Community members expressed frustration at the tendency of scientists to treat animals as numbers.

(Adapted from Nadasdy, 1999)

**Figure 4.9 Dall sheep live in mountainous regions around the Yukon
Territory and Alaska**

In the debate described in Box 4.4, both the scientists and the local residents
want to protect the population of Dall sheep. Both take a holistic view,
looking out for the future of these animals. The scientists were probably
worried about the loss of female sheep (as potential mothers) under a quota
system – a quantitative and biological view of the sheep. But members of
the indigenous community around Kluane Lake were more concerned
about how the animals think, behave and relate to one another – a
qualitative and social view of the sheep. Such phenomena could not be
plotted on maps, nor calculated as birth rates and future population figures.
Since the Kluane people in the Yukon are not part of the Inuit culture (they
are of Athapascan Indian ancestry), the example does not actually involve
IQ. Nonetheless, it does illustrate how *IQ*'s third guideline (*avatimik
kamattiarniq*) regarding environmental stewardship is not as
straightforward and universal as it first appears. Culture, in other words,
makes a difference.

Activity 4.5   What does a polar bear mean? (Take 2)

You first saw reference to polar bears in Block 1 of this course with two
newspaper articles about changes in the numbers of polar bears in the Arctic,
and polar bears have appeared earlier in Block 2 as well. In Part 1, you saw
their images in media and campaigns in the industrialised world about climate
change, and you have since read about their habitat and their significance to
Inuit people. Look back at the two images in Figures 1.41 and 1.42 in Part 1.
Write up your thoughts on the significance of polar bears to the environmental
activist in East Anglia and to the woman preparing the bear skin in these
images. In what ways is their understanding of the polar bear similar? In what
ways is their understanding probably different?

Discussion

One of the differences in their understanding of polar bears is whether they see the animal as a helpless victim. The activist argues that humans are partly responsible for climate change, and polar bears are the helpless victims of the consequences. The Inuit woman, however, probably could not do what is shown in the image if she considered it to be a helpless victim. She may see the animal as a willing participant in her ecological community. Thus the kind of respect that these two people hold for the animal is probably quite different (and you will learn more about such conflicts in the next block). But these two views have similar implications, and that is important: both environmentalists and Inuit people generally are concerned about rapid changes in polar bear habitat.

Over the last few pages I have asked you to consider two of the guidelines for *Inuit Qaujimajatuqangit* (*IQ*) which, again, roughly means 'long-standing Inuit ways of knowing'. In regard both to the stewardship of nature and to treating wildlife with respect, small but significant differences suggest that *IQ* may not be as familiar as a list of its principles (in English) makes it appear. These are the differences that culture and language can make.

Summary of Section 4

Having explored some of the context in which many Inuit people generate TEK, Section 4 returned to the question of what, exactly, is 'traditional' about this form of knowledge. Where many scientists expect it to consist of stories and legends, you learned that skilled (or tacit) knowledge is a dynamic and key component to TEK, and to that which it can offer to environmental researchers as well. The section then reviewed a proposal for an alternative name for this form of indigenous knowledge, abbreviated as *IQ*. Two of the major guidelines for *IQ* – those regarding respect for wildlife and environmental stewardship – were shown to be ideas that do not necessarily translate entirely from an Inuit context into what is commonly understood as 'respect' and 'stewardship' in the industrialised (or 'western') world. Culture, in short, makes a difference.

Science and traditional ecological knowledge

5

You may recall that elders in the eastern Canadian Arctic started to spell out *IQ* as an indigenous alternative to what environmental researchers were calling TEK, traditional ecological knowledge. Again, language was part of the problem, in part because the idea of 'tradition' was misleading in many ways. If you keep two things in mind – first, that the cross-cultural use of TEK quickly gets complicated, and second, that most environmental scientists are even less familiar with the thinking behind *IQ* – then it probably makes sense why scientific publications and papers using Inuit knowledge still tend to be illustrative. That is, articles on the subject usually show how such studies can be done, and usually by way of an example. That is because researchers often run into some unexpected dilemmas when they first start working with Inuit knowledge bearers. These dilemmas can include questions like: How does one establish rapport within a community? How does one ask a good question in that community? How does one make sense of unexpected results? Does everyone in the room mean the same thing when they use the same words? Through illustrative studies, scientists have been sharing different approaches to these dilemmas.

Box 4.5 draws from one such study. Its author, Sheri Fox, was interested in climate change in four Arctic communities in Canada. She discusses some of the methods she has used in her work. Her methods include learning some of the indigenous Inuktitut language, working with local elders, and living in the Arctic villages for months at a time to get to know each community and to build trust. Here she describes a research trend (it is one reason why you will probably see more about TEK in coming years), and then she explains why work that uses TEK is important in her own field.

Box 4.5   A climate-change geographer writes on Inuit perspectives

… Despite a wealth of empirical knowledge held by the Inuit about climate change, scientific research on this topic, which has been going on with much vigour in the Arctic for decades, has rarely included observations by local people. Mainly, this is because science has been unable (and often unwilling) to recognize and accept the knowledge of indigenous people as valid and functional. During the last decade in Canada however, as a number of research projects and government agencies began to demonstrate the value and utility of TEK, it began to gain acceptance. …

Arctic climate change is usually addressed on a scale that does not allow for regional or local analysis. Often, the kind of data needed for this is not available. Inuit knowledge and observations from different

> communities can help inform scientific analysis on a smaller (local and regional) scale, as well as provide knowledge on the variation in climate change and its impacts. For policy-makers, [the use of Inuit knowledge] helps to elucidate what actions may be appropriate in order to address the needs of specific communities in the Arctic.
>
> *(Fox, 2002, pp. 13–53, 2002)*

As Sheri Fox argues, Inuit TEK can provide researchers with more data about the environment, and particularly valuable data at that. But hers is one response out of many from the scientific community, and there are very different views regarding the way scientific research should relate to TEK on a general basis. How should Arctic environmental scientists approach Inuit TEK (or *IQ*) in their research? The specifics certainly depend on the particular field of inquiry. Biologists, geologists and climate scientists, for instance, have different requirements in the Arctic. But broadly speaking, there are now three distinct, general responses to the question of integrating TEK with scientific enquiry:

1 Specialisation

The longest-lasting response is that scientists cannot integrate TEK because the methods of science are too specialised. Researchers with this view often argue that it was science, not TEK, which got a spacecraft to the moon. Part of this is about the specialised training required in the sciences. Its methods are thought to be too rigorous and too easily compromised. Scientific enquiry certainly involves a great deal of creative problem solving (*isummaksaiyuq*), but it also requires considerable book learning (*ilisayuq*) to better understand what researchers did in the past and to build on that knowledge with care and attention to detail. People who hold this view also argue that, despite the sharp observational skills of its practitioners, TEK can make only limited contributions to science because TEK takes the form of qualitative (rather than quantitative) evidence, and because the explanations offered by TEK are not easily separated from some of its more philosophical components. Thus, people who hold this view are sceptical about the integration of TEK with scientific research.

2 Integration

The second view offers the most optimistic argument. Those who take this position argue that Inuit TEK can be effectively integrated with environmental research, and that the environmental sciences would be substantially improved by doing so. This is because the best traditional knowledge bearers are very careful observers of the environment, who can offer a great deal of information about animal populations, animal behaviour, the conditions and dynamics of ice and snow, and so on. Scientists simply need to modify their methods to make use of the local, experiential and qualitative nature of TEK, drawing more from social scientific methods (surveys, interviews, focus groups, participant observation, and so on) to enable them to integrate TEK with their existing methods. You have already encountered two proponents of this view, Henry Huntington and Sheri Fox.

3   Conflicting interests

The third view is that genuine collaboration between scientists and traditional knowledge bearers is unlikely in current conditions. The view is not that science is too specialised; indeed, it holds genuine integration to be of utmost importance. But in contrast to the integrationist view, this view is not optimistic about the chances of effective integration. Its proponents believe that many scientists choose not to face the challenges of integrating Inuit TEK with their work because they fear their scientific credibility would be undermined. Since credibility is tied to funding, many scientists turn toward precaution. Those who hold this third view sometimes go further. They suggest that scientists who integrate TEK into their research often end up (despite their best intentions) using the ideas of traditional knowledge bearers to the scientists' own ends, disregarding the rights of the traditional knowledge bearers and, in a contentious way, exploiting them. Even when collaborations are successful, it is usually still the scientists who get most of the credit and good salaries for their work, and a conflict of interests takes root. In this view, the consequence is that some traditional knowledge bearers now hesitate to work with environmental researchers. Since it is difficult to build trust in such circumstances, the people who take a conflicting interests view tend to be pessimistic about the genuine integration of TEK and scientific research.

As a participant in environmental studies, you will probably see a lot more debate about TEK in coming years, and that debate will likely build on these three views. But at this point, with what you know and what you have learned, which view best expresses your own response to TEK? You may want to take a moment to consider this question before you move on.

Summary of Section 5

This last section took the issue of cultural differences in knowledge formation into questions about the relationship between science and TEK. Contemporary debates on the topic tend to be framed around three positions or perspectives. The first suggests that science requires too much training, that its methods are too rigorous and specialised, to effectively integrate TEK. The second argues that TEK has much to offer environmental scientists, who simply need to modify their methods to integrate TEK effectively into their research, while the third argues that anything short of genuine integration runs the risk of exploiting traditional knowledge bearers. Much of the discussion about TEK in coming years will probably build on some of these views.

Summary of Part 4

Part 4 has asked what, exactly, is 'traditional' about Inuit TEK, that body of knowledge about the environment held by members of Inuit communities in the Arctic. Scientists are increasingly turning to TEK to learn more about the environment, yet its use in science has been controversial at times. To better appreciate the nature of TEK, Section 2 introduced you to some of the context of modern life around Iñupiaq Eskimo communities of Arctic Alaska. You learned what kind of qualitative information a local newspaper can provide about people and places in other parts of the world. Section 3 considered the roles of socialisation, language and culture in the recent past and how today's traditional knowledge bearers learned about the environment when they were young. Section 4 returned to questions about what is 'traditional' about TEK amidst a culture that is, traditionally, highly adaptive and changing. Inuit people are, in many ways, poorly served by the term TEK, given the tradition of continual adaptation and change. Section 4 then explored some of the principles listed under a proposal for an alternative name: Inuit Qaujimajatuqangit (IQ). Section 5 summarised three contemporary responses to issues regarding how TEK would best be integrated with scientific enquiry. The last of the three views emphasised conflict, and you are about to explore more conflicts in the Nile river basin in the next block. There you will learn about conflicts between the interests of local communities and the wildlife – gorillas especially – in a region where, in contrast to today's Arctic, access to the bare necessities of life (shelter, food and water) is often far from secure.

After completing Part 4 you should be able to:

- appreciate the nature of traditional ecological knowledge (TEK)
- understand the importance of experience, socialisation and language to different forms of thought and the formation of Inuit TEK
- distinguish between quantitative and qualitative analysis in social science
- recognise the contemporary debates about the effective integration of TEK and scientific enquiry.

This block on the Arctic has helped you prepare for the next step in your journey, providing you with some approaches for your future inquiries. In Part 1, you learned about the range of different ways of knowing about environments and how journalists, artists, scientists, explorers, exploiters and indigenous peoples think about the Arctic. You learned how questions might be asked about the media, and about its limits and potentials for conveying environmental issues that are highly complex. In Part 2, you learned about the theory of continental drift, and about the volcanoes found along constructive plate margins. The region around one constructive plate margin, the East African Rift, is the setting for the second half of the next block. In Part 3, you learned about the global flows of air and water, where changes introduced in one part of the planet, like Europe, can affect pollution levels, temperature and rainfall on other continents like Africa or Arctic North America. Finally, in Part 4, you learned about some of the challenges that scientists and wildlife managers in Arctic North America (like those working in the East African Rift region) face when using the traditional ecological knowledge of local community members to build better understandings of the environmental and wildlife dynamics in an area.

Answers to SAQs

SAQ 4.1

1   277.8 kilograms – all types of wild food includes fish, caribou, moose, birds and eggs, berries, and other types. The answer is the sum of all the figures in the far right column: $154.3 + 100.3 + 10.4 + 4.9 + 4.3 + 3.6 = 277.8$ kilograms per person, on average, were harvested over the course of that year.

2   55.6% – divide the answer in 1 into the figure for fish alone, 154.3, and turn it into a percentage: $154.3/277.8 \times 100 = 55.6\%$. Alternatively you can add all the figures in the middle column for total harvests, and divide that into the total harvest of fish: $38\ 256/68\ 906 \times 100 = 55.5\%$. The difference is due to rounding errors in the first procedure. So 55.5% (or a little over half) of all the wild food harvested by residents of this community, by weight, was fish alone.

3   0.76 kilograms – if 277.8 kilograms of wild food were harvested by and for each person, on average, over the course of the year in Shungnak (see above), then 0.76 kilograms of wild food were harvested by each person, on average, on a daily basis: 277.8 kg/365 days = 0.76 kg per day. That's 761 grams of wild food for each person in that community in 2002, which is roughly equivalent to one average kipper every day, or more than three punnets of strawberries daily.

SAQ 4.2

1   The Inuit word *isummaksaiyuq* can be simply translated as 'to cause thought' or to provoke more thoughtfulness by posing a question or presenting a problem.

2   My teaching style since Activity 4.2 has used *ilisayuq*, with its predominance of lecture. The way I offered three examples in a row was even a kind of drill.

3   This answer will vary, depending on your experience.

4   *Socialisation* is defined as the processes and the social interactions through which a person learns to be a member of a group or culture.

5   *Isummaksaiyuq* was one process through which a person practised their patterns of reasoning and learned the effects of their behaviour in the Arctic in the recent past. Thus it was (and may still be) an important form of socialisation around Inuit societies.

SAQ 4.3

1   *Adaptation* is the word that summarises what many people in the Arctic believe to be the central characteristic of Inuit cultures.

2   The word 'traditional' in TEK is problematic in the Inuit context because it paints a picture of opposites, of knowledge that sits in stark contrast to modern science, one that could be seen as unchanging and even backward.

3   Storied TEK is 'traditional' in the sense that it is acquired with the songs, legends and stories that each generation receives and passes along to the next.

4   Skilled TEK is 'traditional' in the sense that each person develops their own in the context of similar work undertaken by an older generation of family and friends.

5   In the tradition of scientists, a true statement about the general tendencies of wind direction in an Arctic locale would be desirable. Yet many Inuit elders might consider the same statement of fact to be dangerously misleading or, at best, too vague to be useful.

References

Arnakak, J. (2000) 'What is Inuit Qaujimajatuqangit?', *Nunatsiaq News*, 25 August, p. 11.

Briggs, J. (1998) *Inuit Morality Play: The Emotional Education of a Three-Year-Old*, New Haven, Yale University Press.

Fox, S. (2002) 'These are things that are really happening: Inuit perspectives on the evidence and impacts of climate change in Nunavut', pp. 13–53 in Krupnik and Jolly.

Huntington, H. P. (2000) 'Using traditional ecological knowledge in science: methods and applications', *Ecological Applications,* vol. 10, no. 5, pp. 1270–74.

Ipsen, B. (2007) 'Northern youth recognized for contributions', *Arctic Sounder,* 1 February, pp. 1, 4.

Krupnik, I. and Jolly, D. (eds) (2002) *The Earth is Faster Now: Indigenous Observations of Arctic Environmental Change*, Fairbanks, Alaska, Smithsonian.

Kunuk, Z. (2001) *Ajainaa! (Almost!)*, Nunavut, Igloolik Isuma Productions, http://www.isuma.tv/?site/displayFilm/id/18 (Accessed November 2008).

Magdanz, J., Walker, R. and Paciorek, R. (2004) *The Subsistence Harvests of Wild Foods by Residents of Shungnak, Alaska, 2002: Technical Paper 279,* Juneau, Alaska, Division of Subsistence.

Nadasdy, P. (1999) 'The politics of TEK: power and the 'integration' of knowledge', *Arctic Anthropology*, vol. 36, no. 1, pp. 1–18.

Simon, M. (1995) 'New directions for Inuit knowledge and western science', excerpts from a seminar in Iceland regarding 'The importance of indigenous knowledge'.

Wenzel, G. (2004) 'From TEK to IQ: *Inuit Qaujimajatuqangit* and Inuit cultural ecology', *Arctic Anthropology,* vol. 41, no. 2, pp. 238–50.

Acknowledgements

Grateful acknowledgement is made to the following sources:

Text

Page 86: Sammy Cahn and Jule Styne; Box 4.2: From The Arctic Sounder, 13 July 2006;

Figures

Figure 1.1: Courtesy of NASA at http://visibleearth.nasa.gov; Figure 1.2: © Royal Geographical Society Picture Library; Figure 1.7: Courtesy of Carlos A. Furuti at www.prognos.com/furuti; Figure 1.8: Courtesy of Joe Smith; Figure 1.9: Courtesy of Mark Brandon; Figure 1.10: Courtesy of Anchorage Museum; Figure 1.11: National Snow and Ice Data Center; Figure 1.12: Compiled by Dallmann, W.K. from Norway Polar Institute and Schweitzer, P. from University of Alaska, Fairbanks; Figure 1.13: Courtesy of National Oceanic and Atmospheric Administration, US Dept. of Commerce; Figure 1.14: Data from NASA Earth Observing System Advanced Microwave Scanning Radiometer (AMSR-E); images from Institute of Environmental Physics at the University of Bremen. Animation credit: National Snow and Ice Data Center; Figure 1.15: Data from SAR; Alaska Satellite Facility (ASF) at the University of Alaska, Fairbanks; Figure 1.16: © Rob Magee/BBC News; Figure 1.17: National Snow and Ice Data Center; Figure 1.18: © News International Syndication Ltd; Figure 1.19: © Catherine Ashmore; Figure 1.20: © Bridgeman Art Library; Figure 1.21: Taken from www.findagrave.com; Figure 1.22: Courtesy of Cape Farewell; Figure 1.23: Dancer: Sarah Warsop, Choreographer: Siobhan Davies, Photograph: with thanks to the Natural History Museum; Figure 1.24: Dancer: Sarah Warsop, Choreographer: Siobhan Davies, Photograph: Marije de Haas; Figure 1.25: Courtesy of Cape Farewell; Figure 1.26: © The Print Collector/Alamy; Figure 1.27: © AKG-images; Figure 1.28: The Art Archive/British Museum/Harper Collins Publishers; Figure 1.29: Courtesy of Jonathan Dore; Figure 1.30: © Royal Geographical Society Picture Library; Figure 1.31: © Mary Evans Picture Library; Figure 1.33: © Michigan Technological University Archives and Copper Country Historical Collections; Figures 1.34, 1.35 and 1.36: Courtesy of Alex Hartley; Figure 1.37: © PA Photos; Figure 1.38: Courtesy of USGS; Figure 1.39: Courtesy of Vincent K. Chan; Figure 1.40: Courtesy of www.theodora.com/flags used with permission; Figure 1.41: © Royal Geographical Society Picture Library; Figure 1.42: Courtesy of Joe Smith; Figure 1.43: Religion, Science and Environment/Dan Heaf;

Figure 2.1: Taken from www.wikimedia.org (Halvard, Norway) and used under GNU Free Documentation Licence; Figure 2.3: © Alan Holiday; Figure 2.5a and b: Taken from www.wikipedia.org and used under Creative Commons Attribution 2.5 Licence; Figure 2.6a and b: Reproductions of the original maps courtesy of University of California, Berkeley; Figure 2.7: Courtesy of USGS; Figure 2.10: © FLPA/Alamy; Figure 2.11: Taken from